Collins

C000179862

A2 Revision**Notes**

Chemistry

• George Facer •

Series editor: Jayne de Courcy

William Collins' dream of knowledge for all began with the publication of his first book in 1819. A self-educated mill worker, he not only enriched millions of lives, but also founded a flourishing publishing house. Today, staying true to this spirit, Collins books are packed with inspiration, innovation and practical expertise. They place you at the centre of a world of possibility and give you exactly what you need to explore it.

Collins. Do more.

Published by Collins
An imprint of HarperCollins*Publishers*
77 – 85 Fulham Palace Road
Hammersmith
London
W6 8JB

10 9 8 7 6 5 4 3 2 1

ISBN-13 978 0 00 720690 2
ISBN-10 0 00 720690 9

British Library Cataloguing in Publication Data
A Catalogue record for this publication is available from the British Library

Edited by Ros Davies
Production by Katie Butler
Series design by Sally Boothroyd
Illustrations by Kathy Baxendale
Index compiled by Indexing Specialists (UK) Ltd
Printed and bound by Printing Express, Hong Kong

HOW THIS BOOK WILL HELP YOU

We have planned this book to make your revision as easy and effective as possible.

Here's how:

SHORT, ACCESSIBLE NOTES THAT YOU CAN INTEGRATE INTO YOUR REVISION FILE

Collins Revision Notes A2 Chemistry has been prepared by a top examiner who knows exactly what you need to revise in order to be successful.

You can *either* base your revision on this book *or* you can tear out the notes and integrate them into your own revision file. This will ensure that you have the best possible notes to revise from.

STUDENT-FRIENDLY PRESENTATION

The notes use lots of visual aids – diagrams, tables, flowcharts, etc. – so the content is easier to remember.

There is also systematic use of colour to help you revise:

MUST REMEMBER
Red panels highlight essential content.

MUST TAKE CARE
Purple panels highlight areas where students often make mistakes.

– Red type identifies key terms.
– Green type identifies key definitions.
– Yellow highlight is used to emphasise important words and phrases.

CONTENT MATCHED TO YOUR SPECIFICATION

The Contents/Specification Matching Grid on pages iv-v lists each short topic and shows which specifications it is relevant to. This means you know exactly which topics you need to revise.

In some topics, there are short sections that are only relevant to one or two specifications. These are clearly marked.

GUIDANCE ON EXAM TECHNIQUE

This book concentrates on providing you with the best possible revision notes.

Worked examples are also included to help you with answering exam questions. If you want more help with exam technique, then use the exam practice book alongside these Revision Notes: *Collins Do Brilliantly A2 Chemistry*.

Using both these books will help you to achieve a high grade in your A2 Chemistry exams.

CONTENTS

LATTICE ENERGY AND THE BORN HABER CYCLE

TRUE OR EXPERIMENTAL VALUE

- Calculated from Born Haber cycle.
- Depends on:
  - magnitude of the charge: the larger the charge, the larger the lattice energy
  - sum of the radii of the cation and the anion: small radii result in large lattice energy
  - good ratio of size: reduces repulsion between ions of like charge
  - extent of covalency: highly polarising cations (small radius and/or large charge) and polarisable anions (large ions like I^-) result in compound being significantly covalent.

Causes value from BH cycle to be more **exothermic** than theoretical value

THEORETICAL VALUE

- Calculated assuming compund to be 100% ionic from:
  - charge of ions
  - radius of ions
- Depends only on:
  - charge
  - radius
  - arrangement
  - relative size of the ions

LATTICE ENERGY

- For $MgCl_2$ it is the energy change, per mole, for:
  $Mg^{2+}(g) + 2Cl^-(g) \rightarrow MgCl_2(s)$
- Defined this way, values of lattice energy are always negative (exothermic).

DEFINITION

Lattice energy is the energy change when 1 mol of an ionic solid is formed from its separate gaseous ions.

- Edexcel, Nuffield and OCR only allow this definition of lattice energy.
- AQA allows this definition but also lets it be stated in the other direction – the **dissociation** of 1 mol of an ionic solid into separate gaseous ions.

WORKED EXAMPLE

Why is the lattice energy of CaF_2 greater than that of KF?

The calcium **ion** is **2+** and has a **smaller radius** than the singly plus potassium ion.

WORKED EXAMPLE

The experimental values of lattice energy, with the theoretical value in brackets, are for KF –817 (–807) kJ mol^{-1} and for MgI_2 –2327 (–1944) kJ mol^{-1}.

Explain why the experimental and theoretical values for KF are similar whereas they differ considerably for MgI_2.

The K ion is 1+ and fairly large so it **does not polarise** the F^- ion. This causes the bond to be almost **100% ionic** so the two lattice energy values are similar. The Mg ion is 2+ and has a much smaller radius so it is **strongly polarising**. The I^- ion is very big and is easily polarised. These two factors cause MgI_2 to be significantly **covalent** and increase the numerical value of the lattice energy over the theoretical value.

- The sign in all thermochemical quantities – e.g. lattice energy and ΔH_f – gives direction of heat change.
- –1000 kJ is a larger heat change than –500 kJ.

MUST REMEMBER

- **Exothermic** changes have a **minus** value.
- **Endothermic** changes have a **positive** value.

BORN HABER CYCLE

Born Haber cycle is an example of Hess's law.

- Direct route is the enthalpy of formation of an ionic solid:

  Elements (in their standard states) → solid ionic compound

- Indirect route is:

  Atomising the elements + ionising the metal + the electron affinity of the non-metal + the lattice energy

$\Delta H_{formation}$ = the sum of the enthalpy changes in the indirect route

- Any enthalpy change can be calculated from knowing the values of all the others.

Definition	Examples
Enthalpy of atomisation of an element, ΔH_a: enthalpy change when 1 mol of atoms is formed from the element in its standard state	Enthalpy change per mole for $Mg(s) \rightarrow Mg(g)$ $\frac{1}{2}Cl_2(g) \rightarrow Cl(g)$ $\frac{1}{2}Br_2(l) \rightarrow Br(g)$ $\frac{1}{4}P_4(s) \rightarrow P(g)$
Enthalpy of atomisation of a compound: enthalpy change when 1 mol of the gaseous compound is dissociated into gaseous atoms	Enthalpy change per mole for $CH_4(g) \rightarrow C(g) + 4H(g)$
1st ionisation energy: energy change when one electron is removed from each of 1 mol of gaseous atoms	Energy change per mole for $Mg(g) \rightarrow Mg^+(g) + e^-$ $Cl(g) \rightarrow Cl^+(g) + e^-$
2nd ionisation energy: energy change when one more electron is removed from each of 1 mol of gaseous singly positive ions	Energy change per mole for $Mg^+(g) \rightarrow Mg^{2+}(g) + e^-$
1st electron affinity of an element, EA: energy change when 1 mol of gaseous atoms gain 1 electron each	Energy change per mole for $Cl(g) + e^- \rightarrow Cl^-(g)$
Enthalpy of formation, ΔH_f: enthalpy change when 1 mol of the substance is formed from its elements in their standard states (e.g. $Cl_2(g)$ or $Br_2(l)$)	Energy change per mole for $Na(s) + \frac{1}{2}Cl_2(g) \rightarrow NaCl(s)$ $Fe(s) + \frac{3}{2}Br_2(l) \rightarrow FeBr_3(s)$

MUST REMEMBER

All **standard enthalpy changes** are measured at:

- **101 kPa (1 atm) pressure**
- **a stated temperature (usually 298K)**

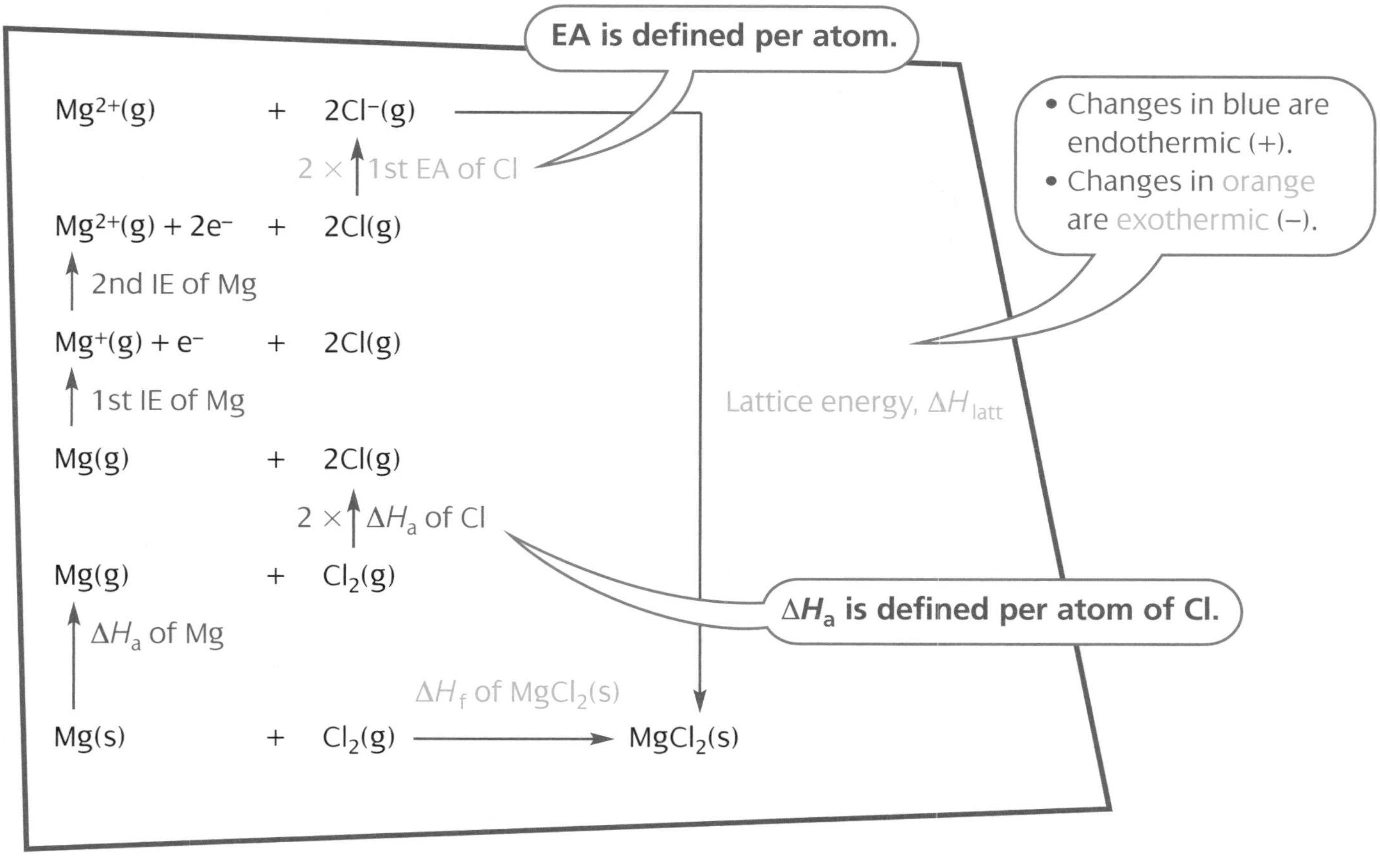

This can also be drawn as an energy level diagram. This shows whether enthalpy change is:

- endothermic ↑
- exothermic ↓

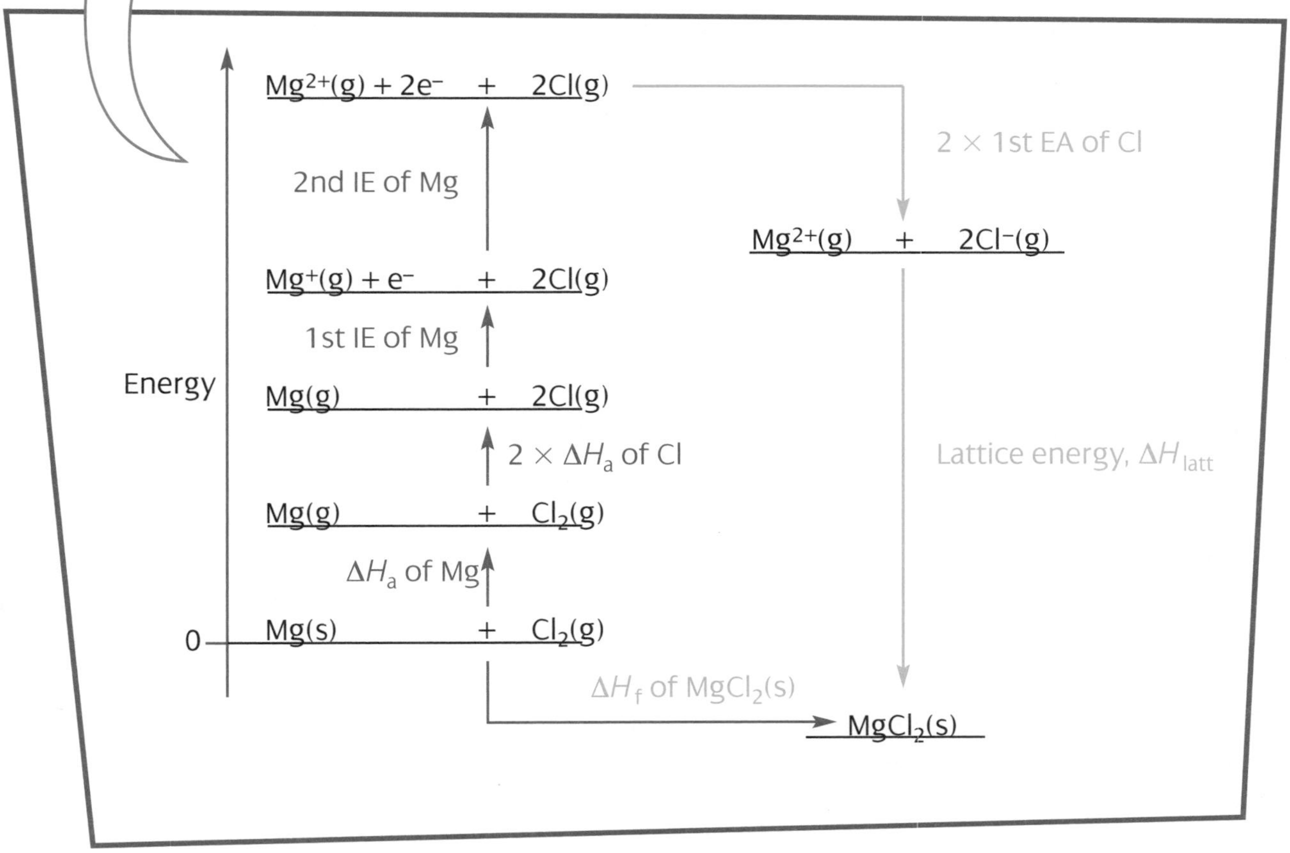

WORKED EXAMPLE

Use the Born Haber cycle on the previous page and the data below to calculate the lattice energy of magnesium chloride.

	ΔH / kJ mol^{-1}		ΔH / kJ mol^{-1}
ΔH_a of Mg	+150	ΔH_a of Cl	+121
1st IE of Mg	+736	EA of Cl	–364
2nd IE of Mg	+1450	ΔH_f of $MgCl_2$(s)	–642

$\Delta H_f = \Delta H_a(\text{Mg}) + \text{1st IE (Mg)} + \text{2nd IE (Mg)} + 2 \times \Delta H_a\text{(Cl)} + 2 \times \text{EA (Cl)} + \Delta H_{latt}$

$\Delta H_{latt} = -642 - (+150) - (+736) - (+1450) - 2 \times (+121) - 2 \times (-364)$

$= -2492$ kJ mol^{-1}

KEY POINTS

- Lattice energy of an ionic solid depends on:
  - charge of the ions
  - radii of the ions
  - extent of covalency in the bond
- ΔH_a of an element is stated per gaseous atom formed:
  - e.g. enthalpy change for $Cl_2(g) \rightarrow 2Cl(g)$ is $2 \times \Delta H_a$ of chlorine
- Enthalpy change for a gaseous metal $M(g) \rightarrow M^{2+}(g)$ ions is:
  - sum of 1st and 2nd ionisation energies of the metal
- Ionisation energies: always endothermic (positive)
- 1st electron affinities: always exothermic (negative)
- 2nd electron affinities: always endothermic… because a negative electron is being added to a negative ion so has to overcome repulsion

FORMULAE OF IONS

Born Haber cycles explain why magnesium forms $MgCl_2$ whereas sodium forms NaCl when each metal is reacted with chlorine.

- Enthalpy of formation of MgCl(s) can be estimated as –137 kJ mol^{-1}
- Enthalpy change for
  $2MgCl(s) \rightarrow MgCl_2(s) + Mg(s)$
  $= \Delta H_f(MgCl_2) - 2\Delta H_f(MgCl)$
  $= -642 - (2 \times -137)$
  $= -368$ kJ mol^{-1}
- As this reaction is highly exothermic (and entropy is favourable as well), it is highly likely to be spontaneous… so magnesium will not form magnesium(I) chloride.
- If it did, it would spontaneously disproportionate into magnesium(II) chloride and magnesium metal.

- The formation of sodium(II) chloride, $NaCl_2$, would require huge input of energy to remove second electron from sodium.
- This wouldn't be compensated for by extra lattice energy released.
- 2nd ionisation energy for sodium is much greater than 1st because second electron has to be removed from an inner shell (not the case with magnesium).

PROPERTIES OF IONIC SOLIDS

SOLUBILITY

CAUSES OF SOLUBILITY

- Many ionic solids are soluble in water because:
  1. Ion/dipole forces are set up between ions and water molecules.
     The water molecule is polar. The more electronegative oxygen has δ– charge; hydrogens have δ+ charge. Each positive ion becomes hydrated, with (usually) six δ– oxygen atoms attracted to it.
     Each negative ion also become hydrated, with δ+ hydrogen atoms from water molecules attracted to it. This attraction of positive to negative releases energy.

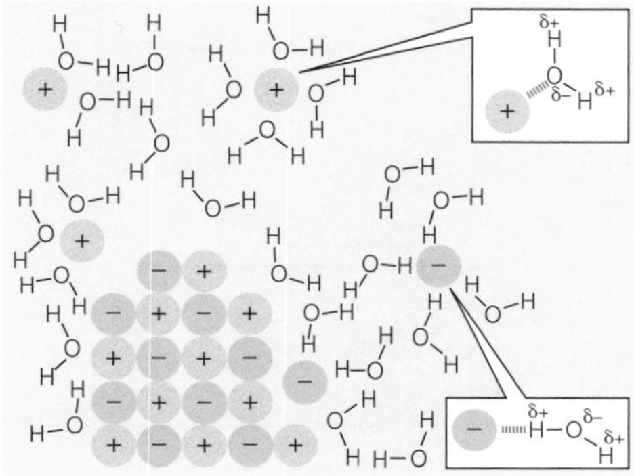

  2. Water's high dielectric constant insulates ions of opposite charge.
     Water molecules surround the ions, acting as insulators which allows the ions to move further apart.
  3. The increase in disorder (or entropy) is a driving force for dissolving a solid.
     Highly ordered solid becomes a randomly arranged solution – this concept is dealt with on page 9.

An **infinitely dilute solution** is one in which there is no further heat change when more solvent is added.

ENERGETICS OF SOLUBILITY

- Some ionic solids give off heat when they dissolve in water; others cool down.
  Depends on whether:
  - exothermic hydration of ions is greater/less than energy required to break up lattice.
- Comparing similar compounds, e.g. hydroxides of Group 2 metals:
  - the more exothermic the dissolving process, the more soluble the compound will be.

Must know the trend in enthalpy of solution:

Substance	ΔH_{soln} / kJ mol^{-1}
$Ca(OH)_2$	−17
$Sr(OH)_2$	−46
$Ba(OH)_2$	−52

(solubility increases ↓)

DEFINITIONS

Hydration enthalpy, ΔH_{hyd}: enthalpy change when 1 mol of a gaseous ion is dissolved in water to give an infinitely dilute solution.

Hydration enthalpies are always **exothermic**.

Enthalpy of solution, ΔH_{soln}: enthalpy change when 1 mol of a solid is dissolved in a solvent to give an infinitely dilute solution.

Enthalpies of solution may be **exothermic** or **endothermic**.

HESS'S LAW FOR DISSOLVING

The **enthalpy change of dissolving** an ionic solid is shown by a Hess's law cycle.

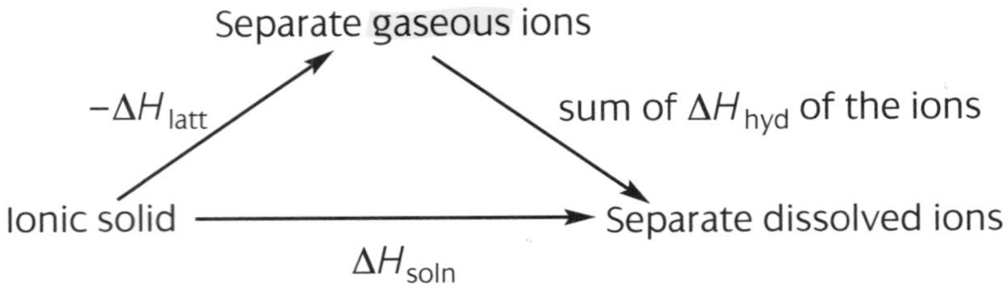

MUST REMEMBER

By Hess's law:
Enthalpy of solution = – lattice energy + the sum of the hydration energies of the ions

If sum of hydration energies > lattice energy
solid will have a negative (exothermic) enthalpy of solution

ENERGY LEVEL DIAGRAMS FOR DISSOLVING

Exothermic dissolving | Endothermic dissolving

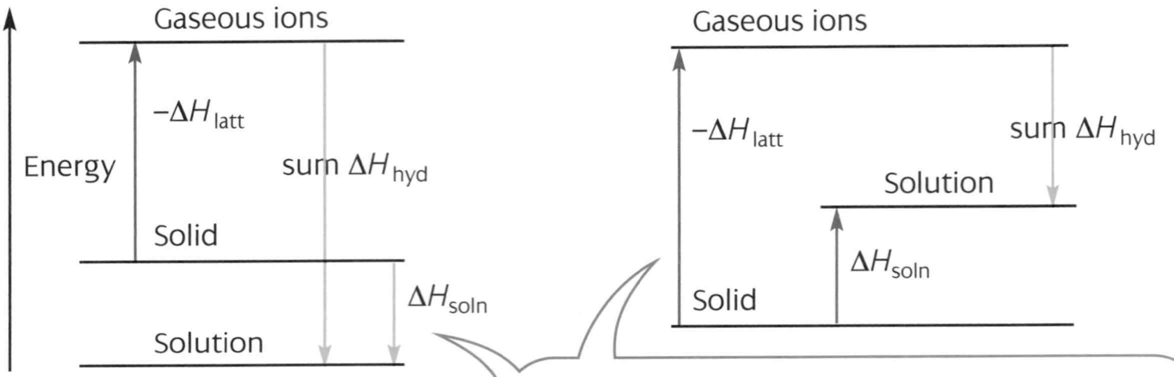

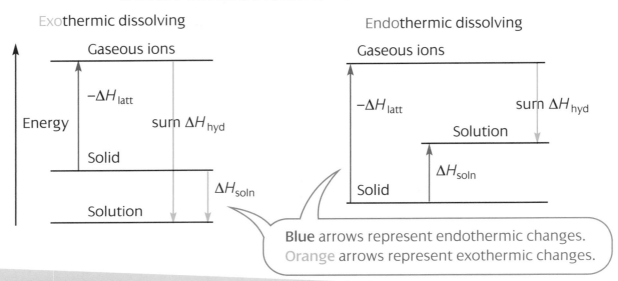

Blue arrows represent endothermic changes.
Orange arrows represent exothermic changes.

WORKED EXAMPLE

Using the data in the table on the right
(a) Draw a Hess's law diagram for the dissolving of calcium hydroxide.
(b) Calculate the enthalpies of solution of magnesium hydroxide and calcium hydroxide and suggest which is the more soluble.

	ΔH/kJ mol^{-1}
ΔH_{hyd} of $Mg^{2+}(g)$	–1920
ΔH_{hyd} of $Ca^{2+}(g)$	–1650
ΔH_{hyd} of $OH^{-}(g)$	–460
ΔH_{latt} of $Mg(OH)_2(s)$	–2842
ΔH_{latt} of $Ca(OH)_2(s)$	–2553

(a) The Hess's law diagram is

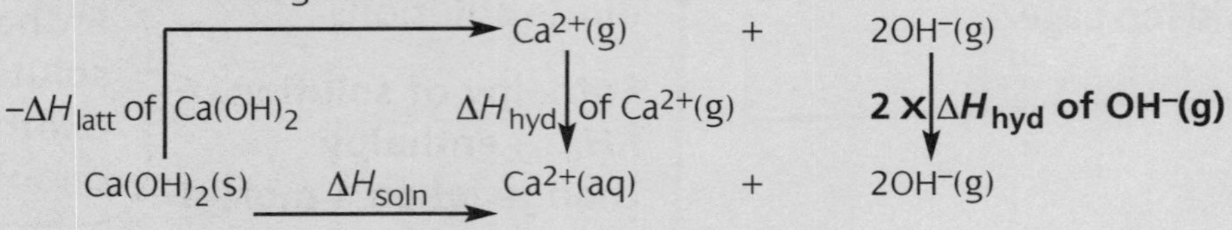

(b) $\Delta H_{soln} = -\Delta H_{latt}$ + sum of hydration energies
ΔH_{soln} of $Mg(OH)_2(s) = -(-2842) + (-1920) + \mathbf{2 \times} (-460) = +2$ kJ mol^{-1}
ΔH_{soln} of $Ca(OH)_2(s) = -(-2553) + (-1650) + \mathbf{2 \times} (-460) = -17$ kJ mol^{-1}
As the compounds are similar, calcium hydroxide probably will be more soluble as it has a more exothermic enthalpy of solution.

VARIATION OF LATTICE ENERGIES IN THE PERIODIC TABLE

IN A GROUP

- For compounds with same anion, **lattice energy** decreases down the Group – because ionic radius increases but ionic charge stays the same.
- As lattice energy depends on the sum of the ionic radii of the cation and the anion, lattice energy decreases:
  - to a greater extent if the cation and anion are of similar size
  - to a lesser extent if the anion is much bigger.
- Hydroxide ion is of a similar radius to Group 2 metal ions.
- Sulphate ion is much bigger than any Group 2 metal ions.

IN A PERIOD

- For compounds with same anion, lattice energy increases across a Period – because the cation's charge gets larger and its ionic radius gets smaller.

VARIATION OF HYDRATION ENERGIES IN THE PERIODIC TABLE

IN A GROUP

- **Hydration energy** of the cation decreases down the Group – because ionic radius gets bigger and the oxygen atoms of the water molecules are bonded less strongly.
- The size of the decrease does not depend on the anion in the Group 2 compound.

IN A PERIOD

- The hydration energy increases across a Period for two reasons:
  1. The charge on the cation increases from 1+ in Group 1 to 3+ in Group 3.
  2. The ionic radius decreases across a Period.

TRENDS IN SOLUBILITY

- **Solubility** of an ionic solid is:
  - decreased by a high lattice energy
  - increased by a high hydration energy.

Solubility determined by the relative value of these two terms.

- Because:
  - highly exothermic changes are more likely to happen than endothermic changes.

GROUP 2 HYDROXIDES

- Solubility of Group 2 hydroxides increases down the Group:
  - The radius of the hydroxide ion is small so similar to radii of Group 2 cations.
  - This causes lattice energy to decrease markedly down the group.
  - Hydration energy also decreases, but to a lesser extent.
  - As the decrease in the lattice energy is greater than the decrease in the cation's hydration energy, solubility increases down the Group.

GROUP 2 SULPHATES

- Solubility of Group 2 sulphates decreases down the Group:
  - The radius of the sulphate ion is large – much larger than any of the Group 2 cations.
  - This causes lattice energy to decrease by a smaller amount than the decrease in hydration energy going down the Group.
  - Thus the exothermic hydration energy decreases more than the endothermic breaking up of the lattice.
  - So sulphates become less soluble down the Group.

MUST REMEMBER

Solubility of $Ba(OH)_2$ > solubility of $Sr(OH)_2$ > solubility of $Ca(OH)_2$ > solubility of $Mg(OH)_2$

Solubility of $BaSO_4$ < solubility of $SrSO_4$ < solubility of $CaSO_4$ < solubility of $MgSO_4$

TRENDS IN STABILITY

CARBONATES

- Carbonates decompose into a metal oxide and carbon dioxide gas.
- Ease of decomposition increases as charge density increases.
- In Group 1: only carbonate to decompose on heating is lithium carbonate – it is smallest cation in the Group so will polarise carbonate ion to such an extent that an O^{2-} ion is removed, leaving $CO_2(g)$.
- In Group 2: decomposition gets harder down the Group – all the cations have a charge of 2+, but the radius increases down the Group, causing the polarising power of the cation to decrease.
- The polarising power of Be^{2+} (very small and 2+) and that of Al^{3+} (small and highly charged) are so great that neither carbonates exist.

charge density = charge ÷ radius

$Li_2CO_3 \rightarrow Li_2O + CO_2$
$Na_2CO_3 \rightarrow$ no reaction

$MgCO_3 \rightarrow MgO + CO_2$

The trend can also be explained in terms of lattice energy:

- As the carbonate ion is a large ion, endothermic breaking up of carbonate lattice does not decrease as much down the Group as exothermic making of the oxide lattice decreases.
- This makes the decomposition more endothermic down the Group and so it does not take place as easily.

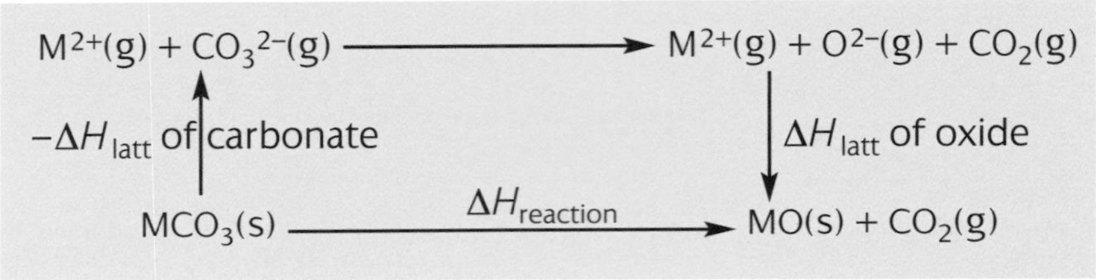

NITRATES

- Group 1 nitrates decompose into metal nitrite and oxygen, except for lithium nitrate – this decomposes into lithium oxide, nitrogen dioxide and oxygen.
- Group 2 nitrates decompose into metal oxide, nitrogen dioxide and oxygen.
- Decomposition gets harder down the Group, as the charge density decreases – caused by the increase in radius.
- Group 2 nitrates decompose more readily than Group 1 nitrates because they have a charge of 2+ which is more polarising than the 1+ charge on the Group 1 cations.

$2NaNO_3 \rightarrow 2NaNO_2 + O_2$
$4LiNO_3 \rightarrow 2Li_2O + 4NO_2 + O_2$

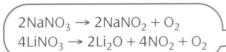

$2M(NO_3)_2 \rightarrow 2MO + 4NO_2 + O_2$

ENTROPY

start

AQA and Nuffield only

Spontaneous changes result in an **increase** in disorder.

- Disorder is measured by a quantity called **entropy**.

- Symbol for entropy: S
- Symbol for change in entropy: ΔS

- 2nd law of thermodynamics predicts the direction of spontaneous change.
- Explains why things happen.
- If you let go of a book it spontaneously falls to the floor:
  - 1st law predicts book could also rise to the ceiling, cooling as it did so.
  - 2nd law predicts that it will only fall.

There is more randomness about the distribution of the energies of the molecules in the hot gas than in the cold gas.

THE EFFECT OF TEMPERATURE

- Hot objects are more disordered – have higher entropy – than cold objects.

Maxwell-Boltzmann distributions of a gas at two temperatures

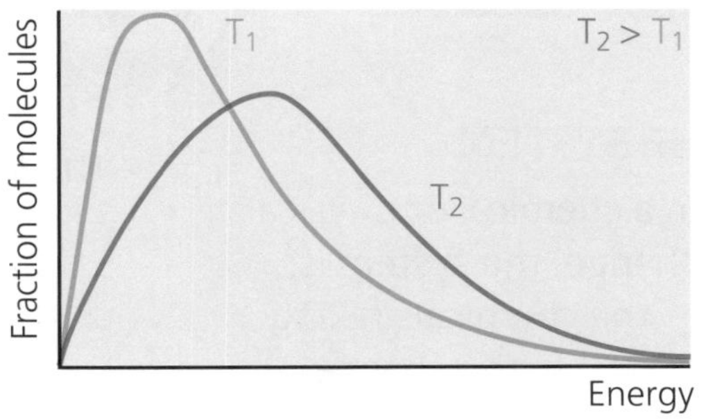

MUST REMEMBER

Rule 1

- If a body **gains heat energy**, its **entropy increases**.

PHYSICAL STATE

- Crystalline solids are highly ordered:
  - each ion or molecule is fixed in position
  - only disorder: atoms in the ions or molecules vibrate.
- Liquids are more disordered and gases even more disordered:
  - molecules can move around as well as vibrate and rotate.

MUST REMEMBER

Rule 2

- **Gaseous state** of a substance has a **higher entropy than the liquid state; liquid state** has a **higher entropy than the solid state.**
- **Solutions** have a **high entropy** – the process of dissolving increases the entropy.

CHEMICAL COMPLEXITY

- The more atoms there are in an ion or molecule, the more ways atoms can vibrate:
  - e.g. calcium carbonate, $CaCO_3$, has a higher entropy than calcium oxide, CaO.

MUST REMEMBER

Rule 3

- More complex compounds have a **greater entropy** than simpler compounds.

EXAMPLES OF INCREASES IN ENTROPY

- The heating of water (cold to hot)
  water at 25°C to water at 35°C
- The vaporisation of water (liquid to gas)
  $H_2O(l) \rightarrow H_2O(g)$
- Dissolving salt: solid + liquid → solution
  $NaCl(s) + aq \rightarrow Na^+(aq) + Cl^-(aq)$
- Adding acid to a hydrogen carbonate:
  solid + solution → solution + gas
  $NaHCO_3(s) + HCl(aq) \rightarrow NaCl(aq) + H_2O(l) + CO_2(g)$

SYSTEM AND SURROUNDINGS

It is essential to distinguish between the **system** and the **surroundings**.

THE SYSTEM

- In a chemical or physical change, the system is:
  - the chemicals taking part in the change.

THE SURROUNDINGS

- The surroundings are:
  - the solvent
  - the container
  - the air in the room where experiment is carried out.

Example	System	Surroundings
1. When water is boiled in a beaker	The chemical H_2O	The beaker The air in the room
2. When a solution of hydrochloric acid is added to a solution of sodium hydroxide in a test tube	The reactants – HCl and NaOH The products – NaCl and H_2O	The air in the room The solvent – water The test tube
3. When the gas is burned in a Bunsen burner	The reactants – methane and oxygen The products – carbon dioxide and water vapour	The air in the room

CALCULATION OF ENTROPY CHANGES

THE SYSTEM

Must use this formula to calculate $\Delta S^\ominus_{system}$ when the standard entropy values at a stated temperature are given.

MUST REMEMBER

$\Delta S^\ominus_{system} = S^\ominus_{products} - S^\ominus_{reactants}$

- If no data supplied, must estimate **sign** of $\Delta S^\ominus_{system}$ by asking:
  - is a gas given off?
  - is there any other change implying an increase in disorder?

WORKED EXAMPLE

Use the data in the table to calculate the value of $\Delta S^\ominus_{system}$ of the reaction

$$CaCO_3(s) \rightarrow CaO(s) + CO_2(g)$$

Substance	Entropy / J K^{-1} mol^{-1} at 298K
$CaCO_3(s)$	93
$CaO(s)$	40
$CO_2(g)$	214

$\Delta S^\ominus_{system} = S^\ominus_{products} - S^\ominus_{reactants}$

$= +40 + 214 - (+93) = +161$ J K^{-1} mol^{-1} at 298K

MUST TAKE CARE

- A sign, in this case a + sign, must always be given in all ΔS and ΔH answers.
- The units of entropy are always in joules per kelvin per mole, not kilojoules per kelvin per mole.

THE SURROUNDINGS

MUST REMEMBER

For both exothermic and endothermic reactions

$$\Delta S^\ominus_{surroundings} = \frac{-\Delta H^\ominus}{T}$$

where $-\Delta H^\ominus$ is standard enthalpy change
T is temperature in kelvin

An exothermic reaction has a **negative** ΔH so the value of $-\Delta H/T$ will be positive.

- **Exothermic reaction:**
  - **surroundings gain heat energy**
  - **entropy of the surroundings increases**

  $\Delta S^\ominus_{surroundings}$ will be positive

The extent of the increase depends on:
- amount of heat released, $\Delta H_{reaction}$
- temperature of the surroundings.

- **Endothermic reaction:**
  - **surroundings cool down**
  - **entropy of the surroundings decreases**

  $\Delta S^\ominus_{surroundings}$ will be negative

MUST REMEMBER

Exothermic reaction:
ΔH **negative** $\Delta S^\ominus_{surroundings}$ **positive**
Endothermic reaction:
ΔH **positive** $\Delta S^\ominus_{surroundings}$ **negative**

THE SYSTEM

WORKED EXAMPLE

Comment on the sign of $\Delta S^\ominus_{system}$ for the following reactions

(a) $NH_4Cl(s) \rightarrow NH_4^+(aq) + Cl^-(aq)$

(b) $NH_4Br(s) + OH^-(aq) \rightarrow NH_3(g) + Br^-(aq) + H_2O(l)$

(a) Solid ammonium chloride is dissolving and so the system becomes more disordered, and so $\Delta S^\ominus_{system}$ increases.

(b) A solid and a solution are converted to a gas, liquid and a solution, and so the disorder increases. $\Delta S^\ominus_{system}$ increases.

THE SURROUNDINGS

WORKED EXAMPLE

Calculate the value of $\Delta S^\ominus_{surroundings}$ for the following reactions at a temperature of 298K

(a) $HCl(aq) + NaOH(aq) \rightarrow NaCl + H_2O(l)$ $\Delta H^\ominus = -57.1$ kJ mol^{-1}

(b) $CaCO_3(s) \rightarrow CaO(s) + CO_2(g)$ $\Delta H^\ominus = +178$ kJ mol^{-1}

$\Delta S^\ominus_{surroundings} = -\Delta H^\ominus / T$

(a) $\Delta S^\ominus_{surroundings} = -(-57.1 / 298) = +0.192$ kJ K^{-1} mol^{-1}
$= +192$ J K^{-1} mol^{-1}

(b) $\Delta S^\ominus_{surroundings} = -(+178 / 298) = -0.597$ kJ K^{-1} mol^{-1}
$= -597$ J K^{-1} mol^{-1}

TOTAL ENTROPY CHANGE

The **total entropy change** is the sum of the entropy changes of the surroundings and the system.

MUST REMEMBER

$\Delta S^\ominus_{total} = \Delta S^\ominus_{surroundings} + \Delta S^\ominus_{system}$

$\Delta S^\ominus_{total} = \dfrac{-\Delta H^\ominus}{T} + \Delta S^\ominus_{system}$

A reaction will be **thermodynamically likely** (spontaneous) if the value of **$\Delta S^\ominus_{total}$ is positive.**

MUST TAKE CARE

The sign and value of $\Delta S^\ominus_{total}$ do not indicate anything about the **rate** of the reaction. The activation energy of the reaction may be so high that the reaction does not take place at room temperature – is said to be **kinetically stable**.

WORKED EXAMPLE

Use the data and answers from the previous worked examples to calculate the value of $\Delta S^\ominus_{total}$ at a temperature of 298K for the reaction

$$CaO(s) + CO_2(g) \rightarrow CaCO_3(s) \qquad \Delta H^\ominus = -178 \text{ kJ mol}^{-1}$$

and comment on its feasibility.

$$\Delta S^\ominus_{total} = \frac{-\Delta H^\ominus}{T} + \Delta S^\ominus_{system}$$

$$\frac{-\Delta H^\ominus}{T} = \frac{-(-178)}{298} = +0.597 \text{ kJ K}^{-1} \text{ mol}^{-1} = +597 \text{ J K}^{-1} \text{ mol}^{-1}$$

$\Delta S^\ominus_{system} = S_{products} - S_{reactants} = +93 - (+40) - (+214) = -161$ J K^{-1} mol^{-1} at 298K

Thus $\Delta S^\ominus_{total} = +597 - 161 = +436$ J K^{-1} mol^{-1}

As $\Delta S^\ominus_{total}$ is *positive*, the reaction is feasible at this temperature.

end

AQA and Nuffield only

STANDARD FREE ENERGY CHANGE

start AQA only

- Chemical potential of a substance is measured by the **free energy**, *G*.
- As with all energy changes, the spontaneous direction of change is to lower the value of the chemical potential energy, *G*.
- The change in standard free energy, $\Delta G^{\ominus}$, is calculated from the following formula.

MUST REMEMBER

$$\Delta G^{\ominus} = \Delta H^{\ominus} - T\Delta S^{\ominus}_{system}$$

- This expression can be derived from:

$$\Delta S^{\ominus}_{total} = \frac{-\Delta H^{\ominus}}{T} + \Delta S^{\ominus}_{system}$$

- Multiplying both sides by –T gives:

$$-T\Delta S^{\ominus}_{total} = \Delta H^{\ominus} - T\Delta S^{\ominus}_{system}$$

- $-T\Delta S^{\ominus}_{total}$ is the change in standard free energy, $\Delta G^{\ominus}$
- As $T\Delta S^{\ominus}_{total}$ must be positive for spontaneous changes, $\Delta G^{\ominus}$ (which equals $-T\Delta S^{\ominus}_{total}$) must be **negative** for reactions that are thermodynamically feasible.

FEASIBILITY OF REACTION

$$\Delta G^{\ominus} = \Delta H^{\ominus} - T\Delta S^{\ominus}_{system}$$

- For a reaction to be feasible, $\Delta G^{\ominus}$ must be negative.
- If $\Delta H^{\ominus}$ is **large** and **negative**, then $\Delta G^{\ominus}$ will almost certainly be negative and the reaction **will be feasible**.
- This is why most exothermic changes are thermodynamically feasible.

- **If $\Delta H^{\ominus}$ is positive, then $\Delta G^{\ominus}$ will only be negative and the reaction feasible if $T\Delta S^{\ominus}_{system}$ is positive and larger than the value of $\Delta H^{\ominus}$.**
- This is why the only endothermic processes that work are accompanied by a significant increase in entropy of the chemicals (the system).

WORKED EXAMPLE

Predict whether the following changes are feasible.

Change	$\Delta H^{\ominus}$/kJ mol^{-1}	$T\Delta S^{\ominus}_{system}$ / kJ mol^{-1}
1	–100	–60
2	–10	–15
3	+10	+15

$\Delta G^{\ominus} = \Delta H^{\ominus} - T\Delta S^{\ominus}_{system}$

Change 1: $\Delta G^{\ominus} = -100 - (-60) = -40$ kJ mol^{-1}.
$\Delta G^{\ominus}$ is negative, so the change is feasible.

Change 2: $\Delta G^{\ominus} = -10 - (-15) = +5$ kJ mol^{-1}.
$\Delta G^{\ominus}$ is positive, so the change will not happen, even though the reaction is exothermic.

Change 3: $\Delta G^{\ominus} = +10 - (+15) = -5$ kJ mol^{-1}.
$\Delta G^{\ominus}$ is negative, so the change is feasible, even though the reaction is endothermic.

EFFECT OF TEMPERATURE ON FEASIBILITY

$\Delta G^{\ominus} = \Delta H^{\ominus} - T\Delta S^{\ominus}_{system}$

Value of the entropy term will alter with temperature.

- If the entropy of the system is **positive** (chemicals becoming more disordered) the value of $-T\Delta S^{\ominus}_{system}$ term will be negative.
- An increase in temperature will make this term even more negative; the value of $\Delta G^{\ominus}$ will become more negative, making the reaction more likely.

- If the entropy of the system is **negative** (the chemicals becoming less disordered) the value of $-T\Delta S^{\ominus}_{system}$ term will be positive.
- An increase in temperature will make this term more positive, and the value of $\Delta G^{\ominus}$ will become positive or less negative, making the reaction less likely.

MUST REMEMBER

- High temperatures favour reactions where the products are **more random** than the reactants. $\Delta S^{\ominus}_{system}$ is **positive**.

MUST REMEMBER

- Low temperatures favour reactions where the products are **more ordered** than the reactants. $\Delta S^{\ominus}_{system}$ is **negative**.

KEY POINTS

- If $\Delta G^{\ominus}$ for the change is negative, the reaction is feasible i.e. the reaction is thermodynamically likely and so is spontaneous.
- Exothermic reactions are thermodynamically likely if the entropy change of the system is positive.
- Exothermic reactions are thermodynamically likely when the entropy of the system is negative, only if the entropy change of the surroundings outweighs the entropy change of the system – this is more likely at lower temperatures.
- Endothermic reactions can only happen if the entropy of the system is positive.
- Endothermic reactions are more likely to take place at higher temperatures.

For practice in answering A2 Chemistry questions, why not use *Collins Do Brilliantly A2 Chemistry*?

end

AQA only

EQUILIBRIUM CONSTANTS

DYNAMIC EQUILIBRIUM

- Most reactions are reversible. When the reactants are mixed, they eventually reach a position of **dynamic equilibrium**.
- When a system is in dynamic equilibrium both forward reaction and reverse reaction are happening but at the same rate.
- At dynamic equilibrium, the concentration of the reactants and products do not alter.
- The **equilibrium constant**, K_c, is a quantity which has a value and units.
- The expression for the equilibrium constant, K_c, is always products over reactants.

LAW OF MASS ACTION

Consider a reaction

$nA + mB \rightleftharpoons xC + yD$

At equilibrium

$$K_c = \frac{[C]^x_{eq} \times [D]^y_{eq}}{[A]^n_{eq} \times [B]^m_{eq}}$$

- *n*, *m*, *x* and *y* are the **stoichiometric numbers** in the equation.

- $[A]_{eq}$ is the **concentration**, in mol dm^{-3}, of substance A at equilibrium.
- **All the values of concentration must be equilibrium values.**

- **The concentration term, sometimes called the quotient, only equals the value of K_c when system is in equilibrium.**
- If concentration term (the quotient) $\neq K_c$, the equilibrium constant, the system will react so that the two become equal.

WORKED EXAMPLE

Consider the reaction

$2SO_2(g) + O_2(g) \rightleftharpoons 2SO_3(g)$

If the equilibrium concentrations are

SO_2: 0.016 mol dm^{-3} O_2: 0.0083 mol dm^{-3} SO_3: 0.15 mol dm^{-3},

calculate the value of the equilibrium constant K_c, stating its units.

$$K_c = \frac{[SO_3]^2_{eq}}{[SO_2]^2_{eq} \times [O_2]_{eq}} = \frac{(0.15)^2}{(0.016)^2 \times 0.0083} = 1.1 \times 10^4 \text{ mol}^{-1}\text{ dm}^3$$

The units can be calculated by realising

$$\frac{\text{conc}^2}{\text{conc}^2 \times \text{conc}} = \frac{1}{\text{conc}}$$

which is

$$\frac{1}{\text{mol dm}^{-3}} = \text{mol}^{-1}\text{ dm}^3$$

WORKED EXAMPLE

What are the units of the equilibrium constant K_c for the following reactions?

(a) $N_2(g) + 3H_2(g) \rightleftharpoons 2NH_3(g)$

(b) $H_2(g) + I_2(g) \rightleftharpoons 2HI$

(a) Units are $\frac{\text{conc}^2}{\text{conc} \times \text{conc}^3} = \frac{1}{\text{conc}^2} = \text{mol}^{-2}\text{ dm}^6$

(b) Units are $\frac{\text{conc}^2}{\text{conc} \times \text{conc}}$ = no units as all the concentration terms cancel

EFFECT OF A CHANGE IN TEMPERATURE

Change of temperature alters the value of the equilibrium constant.

EXOTHERMIC REACTION

- **Increase in temperature causes value of equilibrium constant to decrease.**
- If value of K_c decreases:
  - system is no longer in equilibrium
  - concentration term must get smaller until it reaches same value as new lower K_c
  - **position of equilibrium moves to left, the endothermic direction.**

ENDOTHERMIC REACTION

- **Increase in temperature causes the value of equilibrium constant to increase.**
- If value of K_c increases:
  - system is no longer in equilibrium
  - concentration term must get larger until it reaches same value as new higher K_c
  - **position of equilibrium moves to right, the endothermic direction.**

MUST TAKE CARE

Must not say that an increase in temperature 'favours' the reverse or the endothermic reaction. An increase in temperature speeds up (favours) both reactions, but it increases the rate of the endothermic reaction **more** than it increases the rate of the exothermic reaction.

$N_2(g) + 3H_2(g) \rightleftharpoons 2NH_3(g)$ $\Delta H = -92$ kJ mol^{-1}

WORKED EXAMPLE

For the reaction between nitrogen and hydrogen, state and explain the effect of increasing the temperature on the value of the equilibrium constant and the position of equilibrium.

As the reaction is exothermic, the value of the equilibrium constant, K_c, will decrease with an increase in temperature.
This means that the position of equilibrium has to shift to the left, so as to bring the value of the concentration term down to equal the new lower value of K_c.

$CH_4(g) + H_2O(g) \rightleftharpoons CO(g) + 3H_2(g)$ $\Delta H = +206$ kJ mol^{-1}

WORKED EXAMPLE

For the reaction between methane and steam, state and explain the effect of increasing the temperature on the value of the equilibrium constant and the position of equilibrium.

As this reaction is endothermic, an increase in temperature will cause the value of the equilibrium constant to increase.
This means that the position of equilibrium has to shift to the right, so as to bring the value of the concentration term up to equal the new higher value of K_c.

LE CHATELIER'S PRINCIPLE

This states that if the conditions of a system in equilibrium are altered, the position of equilibrium shifts so as to minimise the alteration of conditions.

- Le Chatelier's principle predicts effect of changing the conditions; it does not explain it.
- It tells you nothing about the effect on the equilibrium constant.

EQUILIBRIUM CONSTANT K_p

For the reaction
$nA(g) + mB(g) \rightleftharpoons xC(g) + yD(g)$

$$K_p = \frac{(p_C)^x \times (p_D)^y}{(p_A)^n \times (p_B)^m}$$

K_p is the equilibrium constant in terms of the **partial pressures** of the gases in the equilibrium reaction.

n, *m*, *x* and *y* are the stoichiometric numbers in the equation.

DEFINITION

The partial pressure of gas A in a mixture of gases is the pressure that the gas would exert if it were alone in the container at the same temperature.

Partial pressure of gas A:
p_A= mole fraction of A × total pressure

Mole fraction of A = $\frac{\text{moles of A}}{\text{total moles of gas}}$

WORKED EXAMPLE

Calculate the partial pressure of sulphur dioxide in a mixture containing 0.016 mol SO_2, 0.0083 mol O_2 and 0.15 mol SO_3 in a vessel at a pressure of 7.0 atm.

Total number of moles = 0.016 + 0.0083 + 0.15 = 0.1743 mol
Mole fraction of SO_2 = 0.016 / 0.1743 = 0.0918
Partial pressure of SO_2 = 0.0918 × 7.0 = 0.64 atm

The sum of all the partial pressures adds up to the total pressure.

Must not use square brackets in any K_p calculations – they are specific to K_c calculations.

WORKED EXAMPLE

Using the data in the table, calculate the value of K_p for the reaction

$2SO_2(g) + O_2(g) \rightleftharpoons 2SO_3(g)$

taking place at a pressure of 7.0 atm.

Substance	Moles at equilibrium
SO_2	0.016
O_2	0.0083
SO_3	0.15

Total number of moles = 0.016 + 0.0083 + 0.15 = 0.1743 mol

Partial pressure of SO_2, $p(SO_2)$ = mole fraction × total pressure
$= \frac{0.016 \times 7.0}{0.1743} = 0.643$ atm

Partial pressure O_2, $p(O_2) = \frac{0.0083 \times 7.0}{0.1743} = 0.333$ atm

Partial pressure of SO_3, $p(SO_3)$ = 7.0 – 0.643 – 0.333 = 6.024 atm

$$K_p = \frac{(p(SO_3))^2}{(p(SO_2))^2 \times p(O_2)} = \frac{(6.024)^2}{(0.643)^2 \times 0.333} = 264 \text{ atm}^{-1}$$

EFFECT OF CHANGE IN PRESSURE

- Alteration of pressure (or concentration) has no effect on value of the equilibrium constant.
- If there are a different number of moles on the left side of the equation to number on the right side, the value of concentration term or partial pressure term will alter.
- If there are more moles on the right, with an increase in pressure:
  - concentration term will get bigger and will no longer equal K_c
  - position of equilibrium will shift to the left to bring value of concentration term back to equalling K_c.
- If there are more moles on the left, with an increase in pressure:
  - partial pressure term will get smaller and will no longer equal K_p
  - position of equilibrium will shift to the right to bring value of partial pressure term back to equalling K_p.

WORKED EXAMPLE

Consider the reaction

$$N_2(g) + 3H_2(g) \rightleftharpoons 2NH_3(g)$$

State the effect on the equilibrium constant and explain the effect on the position of this equilibrium of an increase in pressure caused by decreasing the volume of the reaction vessel.

$$K_c = \frac{[NH_3]^2_{eq}}{[N_2]_{eq} \times [H_2]^3_{eq}}$$

- An increase in pressure has no effect on the value of the equilibrium constant.
- An increase in pressure will increase all the concentrations by the same factor. (Halving the volume will double all the concentrations.)
- As there are more gas molecules on the left, an increase in pressure will increase the bottom line by more than the top line.
- This causes the concentration term to get smaller and no longer equal to the equilibrium constant.
- Nitrogen and hydrogen react to form ammonia, increasing the concentration of ammonia and decreasing the concentration of the two reactants until the concentration term once again equals the unchanged value of K_c.

This is predicted by Le Chatelier's principle – converting many molecules into fewer molecules lessens the increase in pressure.

WORKED EXAMPLE

Predict and explain the effect of a decrease in volume on the following system at equilibrium

$$H_2(g) + I_2(g) \rightleftharpoons 2HI(g)$$

- A decrease in volume increases the pressure.
- The value of the equilibrium constant does not change.
- As there are two molecules of gas on both sides, the concentration term (or the partial pressure term) will not alter.
- As neither alters, the position of equilibrium does not change.

WORKED EXAMPLE

Predict the effect of adding an inert gas, such as argon, at constant volume to the following system at equilibrium

$$N_2(g) + 3H_2(g) \rightleftharpoons 2NH_3(g)$$

- Temperature is the only factor that alters the value of the equilibrium constant of a reaction.
- The addition of the argon increases the total pressure, but does not alter the concentration of any of the three reactants, as the same number of moles are in the same volume. So the position of equilibrium does not change.

This is an example where Le Chatelier's principle would predict the wrong answer.

EFFECT OF CHANGE IN CONCENTRATION OF ONE SUBSTANCE

If the concentration of one substance is altered:

- Value of K_c does not alter.
- Value of concentration term alters.
- System reacts so that the two become equal again.

WORKED EXAMPLE

Explain the effect of adding
(a) acid
(b) alkali
to the equilibrium $2CrO_4^{2-}(aq) + 2H^+(aq) \rightleftharpoons Cr_2O_7^{2-}(aq) + H_2O(l)$

yellow (left), orange (right)

$$K_c = \frac{[Cr_2O_7^{2-}]}{[CrO_4^{2-}]^2 \times [H^+]^2}$$

(a) Addition of acid does not alter the value of K_c, but it causes the value of the bottom line of the concentration term to get bigger.
The system reacts to re-establish equilibrium by reacting left to right, increasing the concentration of $Cr_2O_7^{2-}$ and turning the solution more orange.

(b) Addition of alkali removes H^+ ions, making the concentration term bigger (bottom line smaller).
The system reacts to re-establish equilibrium by reacting right to left, decreasing the concentration of $Cr_2O_7^{2-}$ and turning the solution more yellow.

EFFECT OF A CATALYST

- A catalyst has no effect on value of equilibrium constant.
- It does not alter the concentrations, so has no effect on concentration term.
- It does not alter the partial pressures of any gases, so does not alter value of partial pressure term.

MUST REMEMBER

- Addition of a catalyst has no effect on the equilibrium constant nor on the position of equilibrium. It only allows equilibrium to be reached in a shorter time.

EQUILIBRIUM CALCULATIONS

CALCULATION OF EQUILIBRIUM CONSTANT K_c

WORKED EXAMPLE

2.6 mol of ethanoic acid, CH_3COOH, was mixed with 1.6 mol of ethan-1,2-diol and allowed to reach equilibrium when 1.1 mol of the ester $CH_3COOCH_2CH_2OOCCH_3$, was present. The total volume was 250 cm^3. Calculate the value of the equilibrium constant, K_c.

$$2CH_3COOH(l) + CH_2OHCH_2OH(l) \rightleftharpoons CH_3COOCH_2CH_2OOCCH_3(l) + 2H_2O(l)$$

The method is:

1. Write down the expression for K_c.
2. Calculate the moles of each substance that reacted.
3. Calculate the moles of each substance at equilibrium.
4. Divide these by the volume to get the concentration of each substance.
5. Put the equilibrium values into the expression for K_c.
6. Calculate the answer (to 2 or 3 significant figures) and work out the units.

1. $$K_c = \frac{[CH_3COOCH_2CH_2OOCCH_3] \times [H_2O]^2}{[CH_3COOH]^2 \times [CH_2OHCH_2OH]}$$
2. As 1.1 mol of ester was formed, 1.1 mol of ethan-1,2-diol must have reacted and 2.2 mol of ethanoic acid reacted (as the ratio is 2:1).
3. The moles at equilibrium are:

ester	1.1 mol
water	$2 \times 1.1 = 2.2$ mol
ethanoic acid	$2.6 - 2.2 = 0.4$ mol
ethan-1,2-diol	$1.6 - 1.1 = 0.5$ mol

4. The concentrations at equilibrium are:

ester	$1.1 / 0.25 = 4.4$ mol dm^{-3}
water	$2.2 / 0.25 = 8.8$ mol dm^{-3}
ethanoic acid	$0.4 / 0.25 = 1.6$ mol dm^{-3}
ethan-1,2-diol	$0.5 / 0.25 = 2$ mol dm^{-3}

5. $$K_c = \frac{4.4 \times (8.8)^2}{(1.6)^2 \times 2}$$
6. = 67 **(no units)**

If the data is in grams and not moles, must first convert the mass into moles by dividing by the relevant molar mass.

CALCULATION OF EQUILIBRIUM CONSTANT K_p

The method is:

1. Write down the expression for K_p.
2. Calculate the moles of each substance at equilibrium – if no starting amount is given, assume there was 1 mol of the reactant on the left.
3. Add up all the equilibrium moles to get the total number of moles.
4. Work out the mole fraction of each gas (moles ÷ total moles).
5. Work out the partial pressure of each gas (mole fraction × total pressure).
6. Put these partial pressures into the expression for K_p and calculate its value with units.

WORKED EXAMPLE

When some phosphorus pentachloride, PCl_5, was heated to a temperature T in a container, 78% of it decomposed and the pressure in the container was 2.2 atm.

$$PCl_5(g) \rightleftharpoons PCl_3(g) + Cl_2(g)$$

Calculate the value of the equilibrium constant K_p.

1. $$K_p = \frac{p(PCl_3) \times p(Cl_2)}{p(PCl_5)}$$
2. Assume that there was 1 mol of PCl_5 to start with. As 78% reacted, 0.22 mol was present at equilibrium. 0.78 mol of PCl_3 and Cl_2 were formed.
3. total moles = 0.22 + 0.78 + 0.78 = 1.78
4. mole fraction = moles ÷ total moles
   mole fraction of PCl_3 = mole fraction of Cl_2 = 0.78 / 1.78 = 0.438
   mole fraction of PCl_5 = 0.22 / 1.78 = 0.124
5. partial pressure = mole fraction × total pressure
   partial pressure of PCl_3 = partial pressure of Cl_2 = 0.438 × 2.2 atm = 0.964 atm
   partial pressure of PCl_5 = 0.124 × 2.2 atm = 0.273 atm
6. $$K_p = \frac{0.964 \times 0.964}{0.272} = 3.42 \textbf{ atm}$$

CALCULATION OF EQUILIBRIUM MOLES FROM K_C

This can be done in some cases where the numbers of molecules on the two sides are the same:

1. Write down the expression for K_c (there will always be a mark for this).
2. Assume that x moles of the substance(s) on the left have reacted.
3. Calculate the equilibrium moles of each substance and their concentrations in terms of x.
4. Substitute these values into the expression for K_c and solve for x by taking the square root of both sides.

WORKED EXAMPLE

Calculate the amount of hydrogen iodide at equilibrium when 1.0 mol of hydrogen and 1.0 mol of iodine are heated at a temperature *T* until equilibrium is reached in a container of volume 10 dm³.

$$H_2(g) + I_2(g) \rightleftharpoons 2HI(g) \qquad K_c = 49 \text{ (no units)}$$

1. $K_c = \dfrac{[HI]^2}{[H_2]\,[I_2]} = 49$
2. Let x mol of hydrogen react
3.

	H_2	I_2	HI
Moles at start	1.0	1.0	0
Moles at equilibrium	$1-x$	$1-x$	$2x$
Concentration at equilibrium	$(1-x)/10$	$(1-x)/10$	$2x/10$

4. $K_c = \dfrac{(2x/10)^2}{(1-x)/10\,.\,(1-x)/10} = \dfrac{4x^2}{(1-x)^2} = 49$

Taking the square root of both sides

$$\frac{2x}{(1-x)} = 7$$

$$2x = 7 - 7x$$

$$9x = 7$$

$$x = 7/9 = 0.78$$

As the moles of HI at equilibrium is $2x$, there are 1.56 mol of HI at equilibrium.

CALCULATION OF EQUILIBRIUM MOLES FROM K_P

This is done in the same way, but, as with all K_p calculations, it is more difficult than those using K_c:

1. Write down the expression for K_p (there will always be a mark for this).
2. Assume that x moles of the substance(s) on the left have reacted.
3. Calculate the equilibrium moles of each substance, their mole fractions and partial pressures all in terms of x.
4. Substitute these values into the expression for K_p, simplify it and solve for x.

WORKED EXAMPLE

Calculate the percentage decomposition when phosphorus pentachloride is heated to a temperature *T* at a pressure of 4.0 atm.

$$PCl_5(g) \rightleftharpoons PCl_3(g) + Cl_2(g) \qquad K_p = 9.0 \text{ atm}$$

1. $K_p = \dfrac{p(PCl_3)\,p(Cl_2)}{p(PCl_5)} = 9.0$
2. Let x mol of PCl_5 decompose
3.

	PCl_5	PCl_3	Cl_2
Moles at start	1	0	0
Moles at equilibrium	$1-x$	x	x
Mole fraction	$(1-x)/(1+x)$	$x/(1+x)$	$x/(1+x)$
Partial pressure / atm	$(1-x)P/(1+x)$	$xP/(1+x)$	$xP/(1+x)$

4. $K_p = \dfrac{x^2\,P^2/(1+x)^2}{(1-x)\,P/(1+x)} = \dfrac{x^2P}{(1-x)(1+x)} = \dfrac{x^2P}{(1-x^2)}$

Substituting in the values for K_p and P

$$9.0 = \frac{4x^2}{(1-x^2)}$$

$$9 - 9x^2 = 4x^2$$

$$13x^2 = 9$$

$$x^2 = 9/13 = 0.69$$

$$x = 0.83$$

83% of the PCl_5 was dissociated.

VALUE OF *K* AND EXTENT OF REACTION

- If value of K_c is large it means that the position of reaction is well to the right.
- If value of K_c is around 1, the position of equilibrium is close to being half way.
- If the value of K_c is very small, the position of equilibrium is well to the left.

The equilibrium constant at 400°C for the contact process (SO_2 to SO_3) is 3×10^4 so nearly all the sulphur dioxide is converted into sulphur trioxide.

The equilibrium constant at 400°C for the Haber process is 8×10^{-5} so less than $\frac{1}{2}$% of ammonia is present in the equilibrium mixture at 1 atm pressure.

HETEROGENEOUS EQUILIBRIA

- If the reactants and products of a reversible reaction are not all in the same phase, the expression for the equilibrium constant can be simplified.

For example, the reaction $CaCO_3(s) \rightleftharpoons CaO(s) + CO_2(g)$ is heterogeneous because the carbon dioxide is a gas and the other two are solids.

- The concentration of pure solids or pure liquids is a constant and so is ignored in the expression for K_c.
- Only the partial pressures of gases are included in expressions for K_p; the other substances are ignored.

The solid must be omitted from the expression for K_c

WORKED EXAMPLE

State the expression for K_c for the reaction

$$C(s) + H_2O(g) \rightleftharpoons CO(g) + H_2(g)$$

$$K_c = \frac{[CO] \times [H_2]}{[H_2O]}$$

WORKED EXAMPLE

State the expression for K_p for the reaction

$$CaCO_3(s) \rightleftharpoons CaO(s) + CO_2(g)$$

and calculate the pressure of carbon dioxide when calcium carbonate is heated to 800°C. $K_p = 0.80$ atm.

$K_p = p(CO_2) = 0.80$ atm

The two solids must be omitted from the expression for K_p

CHEMICAL EQUILIBRIUM – SUMMARY

KEY POINTS

- K_c equals the concentrations of the products raised to the powers of their stoichiometric numbers in the equation, divided by the concentrations of the reactants raised to their powers:

$$K_c = \frac{[C]^x_{eq} \times [D]^y_{eq}}{[A]^n_{eq} \times [B]^m_{eq}}$$

- K_p equals the partial pressures of the products raised to their powers divided by the partial pressures of the reactants raised to their powers:

$$K_p = \frac{(p_C)^x \times (p_D)^y}{(p_A)^n \times (p_B)^m}$$

- Effect of change in conditions on the value of the equilibrium constant:

Change in conditions	Effect on equilibrium constant
Increase in temperature	*K* increases for endothermic reactions *K* decreases for exothermic reactions
Increase in pressure – caused by compression	*K* does **not alter**
Change in concentration of one or more substances	*K* does **not alter**
Addition of catalyst	*K* does **not alter**

- Effect of change in conditions on the position of equilibrium:

Change in conditions	Effect on position of equilibrium
Increase in temperature	Shifts in the **endothermic direction**
Increase in pressure – caused by compression	Shifts to the **side with fewer gas molecules**
Increase in concentration of one substance	Shifts to the **other side** of the equation
Addition of catalyst	**No change**

- Calculation of K_c:
  - work out the moles of each at equilibrium
  - divide by the volume
  - substitute into the expression for K_c

- Calculation of K_p:
  - work out the moles of each – often assuming there is 1 mol of left-hand side chemical to start with
  - add up all the moles
  - divide moles of each by total moles to get mole fractions
  - multiply mole fractions by total pressure to get partial pressures
  - substitute into the expression for K_p

- A large value of the equilibrium constant means a large theoretical yield.
- A small value of the equilibrium constant means a poor theoretical yield.

ACIDS, BASES AND pH

DEFINITIONS

- **An acid is a substance that gives an H^+ ion (a proton) to a base.** Acidic solutions are those which contain more H^+ ions than OH^- ions.
- **A base is a substance that accepts an H^+ ion (a proton) from an acid.** A base must have a lone pair of electrons, which it uses to form a bond with the H^+ ion. An alkaline solution is one which contains more OH^- ions than H^+ ions.

BRØNSTED–LOWRY ACID–BASE PAIRS

- Think about the reaction of an acid HA with water: $HA + H_2O \rightarrow H_3O^+ + A^-$
- HA is the acid and H_2O is the base.
- However, if the reaction is an equilibrium reaction: $HA + H_2O \rightleftharpoons H_3O^+ + A^-$ in the reverse reaction the H_3O^+ ions act as an acid and protonate the A^- ions, which act as a base.
- A^- is called the **conjugate base** of the acid HA.
- H_3O^+ is called the **conjugate acid** of the base H_2O.

acid – H^+ → conjugate base
base + H^+ → conjugate acid

- **The stronger the acid, the weaker is its conjugate base.**
- HCl is a strong acid; Cl^- is a very weak conjugate base.
- CH_3COOH is a weak acid; CH_3COO^- ions are a weak conjugate base.

WORKED EXAMPLE

Identify the acid–base conjugate pairs in the following reactions

(a) $NH_3 + H_2O \rightleftharpoons NH_4^+ + OH^-$

NH_3	H_2O	NH_4^+	OH^-
base	acid	conjugate acid	conjugate base

(b) $H_2SO_4 + HNO_3 \rightleftharpoons HSO_4^- + H_2NO_3^+$

H_2SO_4	HNO_3	HSO_4^-	$H_2NO_3^+$
acid	base	conjugate base	conjugate acid

The reaction of conc. nitric acid with conc. sulphuric, producing the $H_2NO_3^+$ ion, is how the electrophile is produced in the nitration of benzene.

pH

- The acidity of an aqueous solution is measured in terms of the concentration of H^+ ions.
- When water ionises: $H_2O(l) \rightleftharpoons H^+(aq) + OH^-(aq)$
- The equilibrium constant K_w for this is:

$$K_w = [H^+] \times [OH^-] = 1.0 \times 10^{-14}\ mol^2\,dm^{-6}\ at\ 25°C$$

- $[H_2O]$ is not included in this expression – because water is the solvent its concentration is constant.
- K_w can also be expressed as pK_w, which is $-\log_{10}K_w = 14.00$ at 25°C.
  - In a neutral solution: $[H^+] = [OH^-] = \sqrt{K_w} = 1.0 \times 10^{-7}$ mol dm^{-3} at 25°C
  - In an acidic solution: $[H^+] > [OH^-]$ and so $[H^+] > 1.0 \times 10^{-7}$
  - In an alkaline solution: $[H^+] < [OH^-]$ and so $[H^+] < 1.0 \times 10^{-7}$

pH SCALE

- The pH scale was invented to overcome the problem of negative powers of ten.
- **Definition: the pH is the negative log to the base 10 of the hydrogen ion concentration.**
  $pH = -\log_{10}[H^+]$
  - A neutral solution, at 25°C, has a pH = 7.00
  - An acidic solution has a pH < 7
  - An alkaline solution has a pH > 7

WORKED EXAMPLE

(a) Calculate the pH of a solution where $[H^+] = 2.34 \times 10^{-3}$ mol dm^{-3}

$pH = -\log_{10}[H^+]$
$= -\log_{10}(2.34 \times 10^{-3})$
$= 2.63$ (solution is acidic)

(b) Calculate the pH of a solution where $[H^+] = 2.34 \times 10^{-10}$ mol dm^{-3}

$pH = -\log_{10}[H^+]$
$= -\log_{10}(2.34 \times 10^{-10})$
$= 9.63$ (solution is alkaline)

Give all pH answers to 2 decimal places.

STRONG AND WEAK ACIDS AND BASES

DEFINITIONS

- **A strong acid is totally ionised in solution.**
  For example HCl is a strong acid:
  $HCl(aq) \rightarrow H^+(aq) + Cl^-(aq)$
- **A weak acid is only slightly ionised in solution (usually less than 4% ionised).**
  Ethanoic acid (and all carboxylic acids) is a weak acid:
  $CH_3COOH(aq) \rightleftharpoons H^+(aq) + CH_3COO^-(aq)$
- **A strong base is totally ionised.**
  Sodium hydroxide is a strong base:
  $NaOH(aq) \rightarrow Na^+(aq) + OH^-(aq)$
  Barium hydroxide is also a strong base:
  $Ba(OH)_2(aq) \rightarrow Ba^{2+}(aq) + 2OH^-(aq)$
  Ammonia is a weak base and so is only partially ionised in aqueous solution:
  $NH_3(aq) + H_2O(l) \rightleftharpoons NH_4^+(aq) + OH^-(aq)$

MUST REMEMBER

- A pH can be negative if the strong acid has a concentration greater than 1 mol dm^{-3}.
- A strong alkali with a concentration of more than 1 mol dm^{-3} will have a pH > 14.
- It is a common error to think that the pH scale runs from 0 to 14.

pH OF STRONG ACIDS

- A strong acid is totally ionised, so $[H^+]$ = [the acid]

- Sulphuric acid is called a strong acid, but only the first ionisation is complete:
  $H_2SO_4(aq) \rightarrow H^+(aq) + HSO_4^-(aq)$
- The second ionisation is reversible and its equilibrium is driven to the left by the H^+ ions from the first ionisation:
  $HSO_4^-(aq) \rightleftharpoons H^+(aq) + SO_4^{2-}(aq)$
- This means that the $[H^+]$ in a 0.10 mol dm^{-3} solution of sulphuric acid is **not** 0.20 mol dm^{-3}, but only very slightly greater than 0.10 mol dm^{-3}.

WORKED EXAMPLE

(a) Calculate the pH of a solution of HCl of concentration 0.135 mol dm^{-3}.

$[H^+] = 0.135$ mol dm^{-3}

$pH = -\log_{10}[H^+] = -\log_{10}(0.135) = 0.87$

(b) Calculate the pH of a solution HCl of concentration of 2.34 mol dm^{-3}

$[H^+] = 2.34$ mol dm^{-3}

$pH = -\log_{10}[H^+] = -\log_{10}(2.34) = -0.37$

pH OF STRONG ALKALIS

- A strong alkali is totally ionised.
  - Alkalis of formula MOH:
    $[OH^-]$ = [the alkali]
  - Alkalis of formula $M(OH)_2$:
    $[OH^-] = 2 \times$ [the alkali]
- The pH can be worked out in either of two ways.
  1. Calculate $[OH^-]$, then $[H^+]$ using the expression $[H^+] = \dfrac{1 \times 10^{-14}}{[OH^-]}$
     Then $pH = -\log_{10}[H^+]$
  2. Calculate $[OH^-]$ then pOH (where $pOH = -\log_{10}[OH^-]$)
     Then $pH = 14 - pOH$

WORKED EXAMPLE

(a) Calculate the pH of a 0.123 mol dm^{-3} solution of sodium hydroxide, NaOH.

$[OH^-] = 0.123$ mol dm^{-3}

Either: $[H^+] = \dfrac{1 \times 10^{-14}}{[OH^-]} = \dfrac{1 \times 10^{-14}}{0.123}$

$= 8.13 \times 10^{-14}$ mol dm^{-3}

$pH = -\log_{10}(8.13 \times 10^{-14}) = 13.09$

or: $pOH = -\log_{10}[OH^-] = -\log_{10}(0.123) = 0.91$

$pH = 14 - pOH = 14 - 0.91 = 13.09$

(b) Calculate the pH of a 0.123 mol dm^{-3} solution of barium hydroxide, $Ba(OH)_2$.

$[OH^-] = 2 \times 0.123 = 0.246$ mol dm^{-3}

Either: $[H^+] = \dfrac{1 \times 10^{-14}}{0.246} = 4.07 \times 10^{-14}$ mol dm^{-3}

$pH = -\log_{10}(4.07 \times 10^{-14}) = 13.39$

or: $pOH = -\log_{10}(0.246) = 0.61$

$pH = 14 - pOH = 14 - 0.61 = 13.39$

THE pH OF WEAK ACIDS

ACID DISSOCIATION CONSTANT, K_a

- When a weak acid is added to water, it partially ionises – **dissociates**.
- Think about a weak acid HA:

$HA + H_2O \rightleftharpoons H_3O^+ + A^-$

$$K_a = \frac{[H_3O^+] \times [A^-]}{[HA]}$$

- $[H_2O]$ is not included in this expression – because water is the solvent its concentration is constant.
- The equation is often simplified as:

$HA \rightleftharpoons H^+ + A^-$, so $K_a = \frac{[H^+] \times [A^-]}{[HA]}$

THE pH OF SOLUTIONS OF WEAK ACIDS

- When a weak acid ionises, it produces H^+ and A^- ions in equal quantities.
- If there are no other sources of A^- ions, it is assumed that $[H^+] = [A^-]$.
- As weak acids are only very slightly ionised, almost all of the acid molecules remain undissociated, and so it is assumed that [HA] = [weak acid].
- This means that the expression for the acid dissociation constant, K_a, simplifies to

$$K_a = \frac{[H^+]^2}{\text{[weak acid]}}$$

or

$[H^+] = \sqrt{(K_a \times \text{[weak acid]})}$

- The pH of a solution of a weak acid of known concentration can be calculated from the value of K_a.
- Also, the value of K_a can be calculated from the concentration and the pH.

WORKED EXAMPLE

Calculate the pH of a 0.123 mol dm^{-3} solution of ethanoic acid. K_a for ethanoic acid = 1.70 × 10^{-5} mol dm^{-3}

$$K_a = \frac{[H^+] \times [CH_3COO^-]}{[CH_3COOH]} = 1.70 \times 10^{-5}\ \text{mol dm}^{-3}$$

$[H^+] = [CH_3COO^-]$ $\quad [CH_3COOH] = 0.123\ \text{mol dm}^{-3}$

$$K_a = \frac{[H^+]^2}{[CH_3COOH]}$$

$[H^+] = \sqrt{(1.70 \times 10^{-5} \times 0.123)} = 0.001\,45\ \text{mol dm}^{-3}$

$pH = -\log_{10}(0.001\,45) = 2.84$

The pH of a weak acid solution is higher than that of a solution of a strong acid with the same concentration e.g. pH of 0.123 mol dm^{-3} HCl = 0.91.

WORKED EXAMPLE

A solution of propanoic acid, C_2H_5COOH, of concentration 0.222 mol dm^{-3} has a pH of 2.77.
Calculate the value of the acid dissociation constant of propanoic acid.

$$K_a = \frac{[H^+] \times [C_2H_5COO^-]}{[C_2H_5COOH]}$$

$[H^+] = 10^{-pH} = 10^{-2.77} = 0.001\,70\ \text{mol dm}^{-3}$

$[H^+] = [C_2H_5COO^-]$; $[C_2H_5COOH] = 0.222\ \text{mol dm}^{-3}$

$$K_a = \frac{(0.001\,70)^2}{0.222} = 1.30 \times 10^{-5}\ \text{mol dm}^{-3}$$

MUST TAKE CARE

Must state the expression for the acid dissociation constant, K_a, in all weak acid calculations. Don't start with the expression $[H^+] = \sqrt{(K_a \times [\text{acid}])}$, because it is not always true – see 'Buffer solutions', page 29.

TITRATIONS AND INDICATORS

TITRATIONS

- In a titration:
  - an alkali is added from the burette to a measured volume of acid until all the acid has been neutralised
  - or, alternatively, the acid is added from the burette to a measured volume of the alkali.
- The **equivalence point** is when neither the acid nor the alkali is in excess.
- The solution at the equivalence point is identical to one made by dissolving the salt.
- An **indicator** is used to determine this point.

INDICATORS

- An indicator for an acid–base titration is a weak acid which has a different colour to its conjugate base.
- The reaction for an indicator whose formula can be represented as HInd is:

$$\underset{\text{colour 1}}{\text{HInd}} \rightleftharpoons H^+ + \underset{\text{colour 2}}{\text{Ind}^-} \qquad K_{ind} = \frac{[H^+] \times [\text{Ind}^-]}{[\text{HInd}]}$$

- Addition of acid, H^+ ions, drives the position of equilibrium to the left and the indicator becomes colour 1 (the acid colour).
- Addition of alkali, OH^- ions, removes H^+ ions and so drives the equilibrium to the right; the indicator colour becomes that of colour 2 (the conjugate base colour).
- The end point colour is a mixture of the two colours.

Indicator	Acid colour	Conjugate base colour	End point colour
methyl orange	Red	Yellow	Orange
phenolphthalein	Colourless	Red	Pale pink

- The strength of an indicator as an acid is measured by its equilibrium constant, K_{ind} or its pK_{ind}, where $pK_{ind} = -\log_{10} K_{ind}$

pH RANGE OF INDICATORS

- An indicator changes colour from its acid colour to its conjugate base colour over a range of pH values.

Indicator	pK_{ind}	pH range	Acid colour	Conjugate base colour
methyl orange	3.7	3.1 – 4.4	Red	Yellow
bromophenol blue	4.0	3.0 – 4.6	Yellow	Blue
bromocresol green	4.7	3.8 – 5.4	Yellow	Blue
bromothymol blue	7.0	6.0 – 7.6	Yellow	Blue
phenol red	7.9	6.8 – 8.4	Yellow	Red
phenolphthalein	9.3	8.3 – 10.0	Colourless	Red

pH OF SOLUTIONS OF SALTS

- Salts contain an anion which is the conjugate base of an acid.
- If the acid is weak, its conjugate base is a weak base and will react with water.
  - For example ethanoic acid is a weak acid, and so sodium ethanoate, CH_3COONa, contains the weak conjugate base CH_3COO^-:
    $CH_3COO^- + H_2O \rightleftharpoons CH_3COOH + OH^-$
    The formation of OH^- ions causes a solution of sodium ethanoate to be slightly alkaline.
  - Hydrochloric acid is a strong acid, and so its conjugate base, Cl^-, is too weak a base to react with water:
    $Cl^- + H_2O \rightarrow$ no reaction
  - Ammonium chloride, NH_4Cl, contains the NH_4^+ ion which is the weak conjugate acid of the weak base NH_3. This means that solutions containing NH_4^+ ions will be slightly acidic due to formation of H^+ ions:
    $NH_4^+ \rightarrow H^+ + NH_3$

KEY POINTS

- Salts of strong acids and strong bases (for example NaCl or KNO_3) are neutral with a pH of 7.
- Salts of weak acids and strong bases (for example CH_3COONa) are alkaline with a pH of nearly 9.
- Salts of strong acids and weak bases (for example NH_4Cl) are acidic with a pH of about 5.

TITRATION CURVES

- When an alkali (base) is added to a known volume of acid, the pH rises in a way which depends on whether the acid and the base are strong or weak.
- If an acid is added to a known volume of alkali (base), the pH falls in a way which also depends on whether the acid or the base is weak.

MUST REMEMBER

An alkali is a base that is soluble in water.

VALUES TO ESTIMATE

1. The pH at the start
   - A solution of a strong acid will have a pH ≈ 1
   - A solution of a weak acid will have a pH ≈ 3
   - A solution of a weak base will have a pH ≈ 11
   - A solution of a strong base will have a pH ≈ 13
2. The volume of the equivalence point
   - This has to be determined from the initial volume of acid (or alkali) and the concentrations of both the acid and the alkali.
3. The pH at the equivalence point
   - For a strong acid / strong base titration, the equivalence point pH = 7
   - For a weak acid / strong base titration, the equivalence point pH ≈ 9 (or slightly less)
   - For a strong acid / weak base titration, the equivalence point pH ≈ 5 (or slightly more)
4. The pH when excess alkali or acid has been added
   - When excess strong base has been added, the pH just less than 13
   - When excess weak base has been added, the pH just less than 11
   - When excess weak acid has been added, the pH just more than 3
   - When excess strong acid has been added, the pH just more than 1
5. The general shape of the curve
   - The curve for a strong base being added to a weak acid has a sharp initial rise. All the other curves start by being fairly flat.
   - The curve has an almost vertical portion at the equivalence point.
   - This vertical section is centered on the equivalence point pH.
   - The curve tails off to the excess pH.

If the acid and the alkali are of equal concentration, the volume of the two solutions will be the same **as long as they react in a 1:1 molar ratio.**

The indicator used for a particular titration must have its **pH range of colour change completely within the vertical portion of the graph.**

THE RULE OF TWO

- A weak acid is 2 units of pH more than that of a strong acid.
- A weak base is 2 units of pH less than that of a strong base.
- The salt of a weak acid and a strong base is 2 units of pH more than that of a salt in which both are strong.
- The salt of a strong acid and a weak base is 2 units of pH less than that of a salt in which both are strong.

STRONG ACID / STRONG BASE

- The addition of 0.10 mol dm^{-3} NaOH to 10 cm^3 0.20 mol dm^{-3} HCl:
  - starting pH ≈ 1
  - volume at equivalence point = 20 cm^3
  - pH at equivalence point ≈ 7
  - pH when excess NaOH added ≈ 13

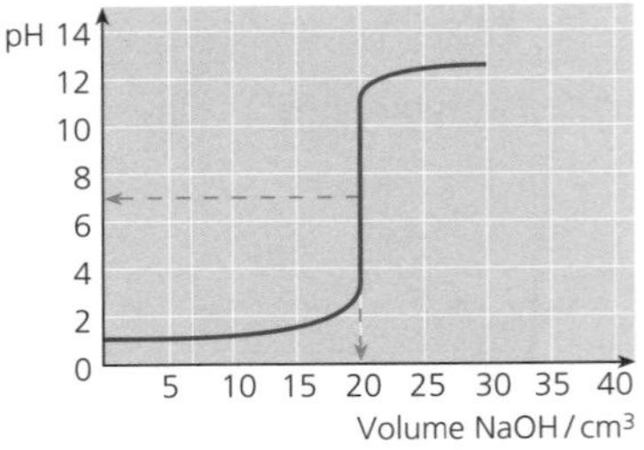

- The addition of 0.10 mol dm^{-3} HCl to 25 cm^3 of 0.10 mol dm^{-3} NaOH:
  - starting pH ≈ 13
  - volume at equivalence point = 25 cm^3
  - pH at equivalence point ≈ 7
  - pH when excess HCl added ≈ 1

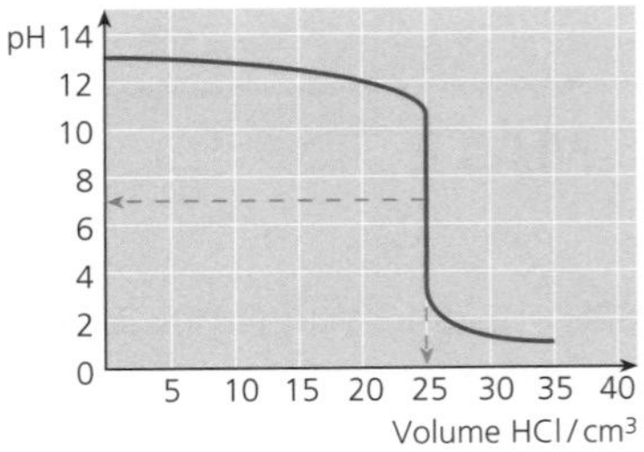

Height of vertical section: range of 8 units, between pH 3 and pH 11.

- For a strong acid/strong base titration any indicator in the list on page 26 will work.

WEAK ACID / STRONG BASE

- The addition of 0.20 mol dm^{-3} NaOH to 30 cm^3 0.10 mol dm^{-3} ethanoic acid:
  - starting pH ≈ 3
  - volume at equivalence point = 15 cm^3
  - pH at equivalence point ≈ 9
  - pH when excess NaOH added ≈ 13

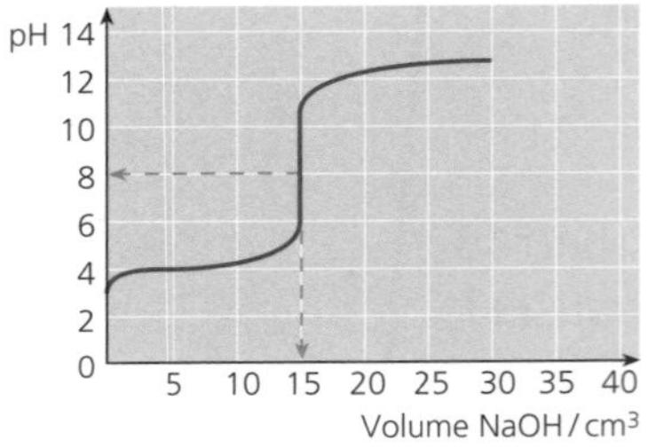

- The addition of 0.10 mol dm^{-3} ethanoic acid to 20 cm^3 of 0.10 mol dm^{-3} NaOH:
  - starting pH ≈ 13
  - volume at equivalence point = 25 cm^3
  - pH at equivalence point ≈ 9
  - pH when excess CH_3COOH added ≈ 3

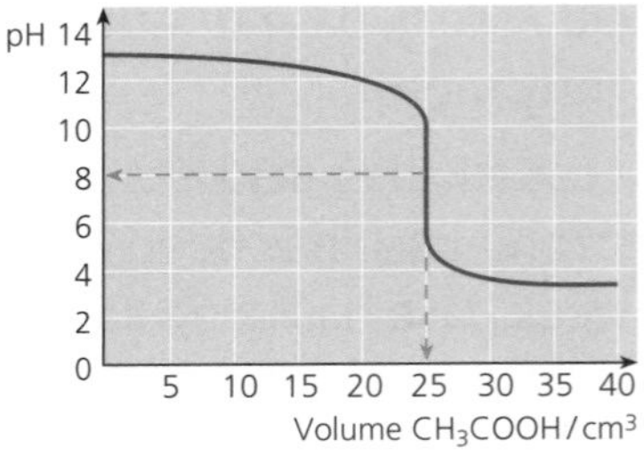

Height of vertical section: range of 6 units, between pH 5 and pH 11.

- For a weak acid/strong base titration any indicator in the list on page 26 whose range lies between 5 and 10, such as phenolphthalein, will work.

STRONG ACID / WEAK BASE

- The addition of 0.10 mol dm^{-3} ammonia to 25 cm^3 0.10 mol dm^{-3} HCl:
  - starting pH ≈ 1
  - volume at equivalence point = 25 cm^3
  - pH at equivalence point ≈ 5
  - pH when excess NH_3 added ≈ 11

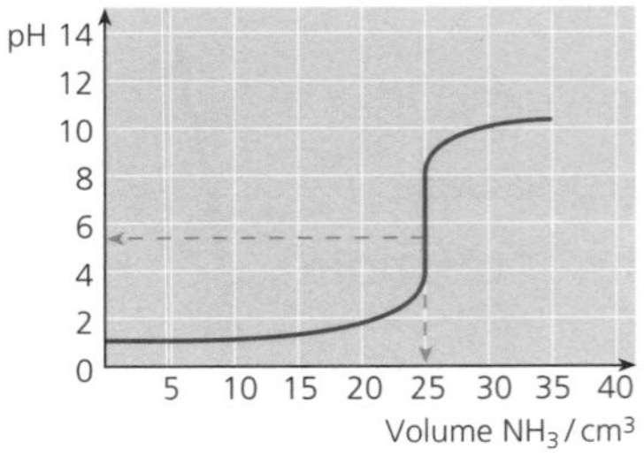

- The addition of 0.20 mol dm^{-3} HCl to 30 cm^3 of 0.10 mol dm^{-3} ammonia:
  - starting pH ≈ 11
  - volume at equivalence point = 15 cm^3
  - pH at equivalence point ≈ 5
  - pH when excess HCl added ≈ 1

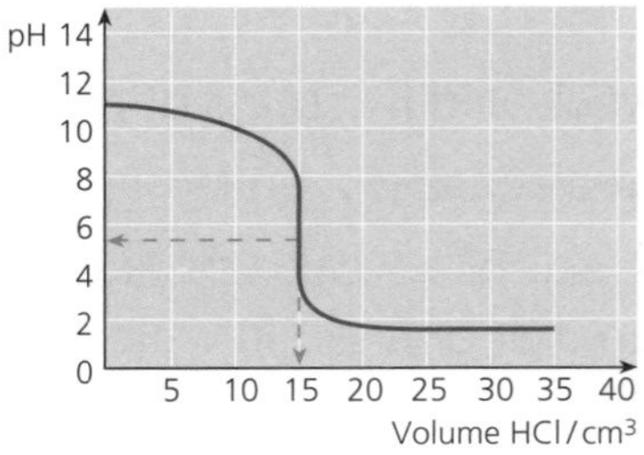

Height of vertical section: range of 5 units, between pH 3 and pH 8.

- For a strong acid/weak base titration any indicator in the list on page 26 whose range lies between 3 and 8, such as methyl orange, will work.

BUFFER SOLUTIONS

DEFINITION

- **A buffer solution has an almost constant pH when small amounts H^+ or OH^- ions are added.**
- **A buffer solution consists of a weak acid and its conjugate base in similar amounts, or a weak base and its conjugate acid.**
  - A mixture of ethanoic acid, CH_3COOH, and sodium ethanoate, which contains CH_3COO^- ions, is a buffer solution. CH_3COO^- is the conjugate base of CH_3COOH.
  - A mixture of ammonia, NH_3, and ammonium chloride, which contains NH_4^+ ions, is a buffer solution. NH_4^+ is the conjugate acid of NH_3.
  - Blood is a natural buffer solution caused mainly by a mixture of hydrogencarbonate ions, HCO_3^-, and carbonic acid, H_2CO_3.

Remember that in a buffer solution $[H^+] \neq [A^-]$

CALCULATION OF pH OF A BUFFER SOLUTION

- Think about a buffer solution made of a weak acid HA and a salt NaA, containing its conjugate base.
- The weak acid is partially ionised:
  $HA \rightleftharpoons H^+ + A^-$
- The salt is totally ionised:
  $NaA \rightarrow Na^+ + A^-$
- The A^- ions from the salt repress the ionisation of the weak acid.
- These two assumptions can be made:
  [HA] = [weak acid added]
  $[A^-]$ = [salt added]
- The expression for K_a is then:

$$K_a = \frac{[H^+] \times [A^-]}{[HA]} = \frac{[H^+] \times [\text{salt}]}{[\text{weak acid}]}$$

$$\text{or} \quad [H^+] = K_a \times \frac{[\text{weak acid}]}{[\text{salt}]}$$

Expression for $[H^+]$ is sometimes written as:

$$pH = pK_a - \log_{10}\left\{\frac{[\text{weak acid}]}{[\text{salt}]}\right\} \text{ where } pK_a \text{ is } -\log_{10}K_a$$

MUST TAKE CARE

It is not a good idea to use this expression because it is easy to forget the sign of the log term or the ratio of [acid] to [salt].

WORKED EXAMPLE

Calculate the pH of a buffer solution made by adding 55 cm^3 of a 0.15 mol dm^{-3} solution of ethanoic acid to 45 cm^3 of a 0.20 mol dm^{-3} solution of sodium ethanoate.
K_a for ethanoic acid = 1.70×10^{-5} mol dm^{-3}

$$K_a = \frac{[H^+] \times [CH_3COO^-]}{[CH_3COOH]} = \frac{[H^+] \times [\text{salt}]}{[\text{weak acid}]}$$
$$= 1.70 \times 10^{-5} \text{ mol dm}^{-3}$$

moles of salt = 0.045 × 0.20 = 0.0090 mol

[salt] = 0.0090 / **0.100** = 0.090 mol dm^{-3}

moles of weak acid = 0.055 × 0.15 = 0.008 25 mol

[weak acid] = 0.008 25 / **0.100** = 0.08 25 mol dm^{-3}

$$[H^+] = K_a \times \frac{[\text{weak acid}]}{[\text{salt}]} = 1.70 \times 10^{-5} \times \frac{0.0825}{0.090}$$
$$= 1.56 \times 10^{-5} \text{ mol dm}^{-3}$$

$pH = -\log_{10}(1.56 \times 10^{-5}) = 4.81$

WORKED EXAMPLE

Calculate the pH of a buffer solution made by adding 20 cm^3 of 0.010 mol dm^{-3} sodium hydroxide to 30 cm^3 of 0.10 mol dm^{-3} ethanoic acid.
$K_a = 1.70 \times 10^{-5}$ mol dm^{-3}.

The sodium hydroxide reacts with the ethanoic acid to form the salt sodium ethanoate.

moles of NaOH = moles of ethanoate ions produced
= 0.020 × 0.10 = 0.002 mol

[salt] = 0.002 / 0.050 = 0.040 mol dm^{-3}

moles of acid left = original moles of acid – moles reacted
= (0.030 × 0.10) – 0.002 = 0.0010 mol

[weak acid] = 0.0010 / 0.050 = 0.020 mol dm^{-3}

$$[H^+] = K_a \times \frac{[\text{weak acid}]}{[\text{salt}]} = 1.70 \times 10^{-5} \times \frac{0.020}{0.040}$$
$$= 8.5 \times 10^{-6} \text{ mol dm}^{-3}$$

$pH = -\log_{10}(8.5 \times 10^{-6}) = 5.07$

CALCULATION OF AMOUNT FOR A BUFFER SOLUTION

- The same expression connecting K_a with [weak acid], [salt] and $[H^+]$ can be used to find the amount of salt that needs to be added to a solution of a weak acid to make a buffer solution of a given pH.

WORKED EXAMPLE

Calculate the mass of sodium ethanoate that is needed to be added to $100\,cm^3$ of a $0.50\,mol\,dm^{-3}$ solution of ethanoic acid to make a buffer solution of pH 4.75.
K_a for ethanoic acid = $1.70 \times 10^{-5}\,mol\,dm^{-3}$.

$[H^+] = 10^{-pH} = 10^{-4.75} = 1.78 \times 10^{-5}\,mol\,dm^{-3}$

$$[H^+] = K_a \times \frac{[\text{weak acid}]}{[\text{salt}]}$$

$$[\text{salt}] = K_a \times \frac{[\text{weak acid}]}{[H^+]} = \frac{1.70 \times 10^{-5} \times 0.50}{1.78 \times 10^{-5}} = 0.478\,mol\,dm^{-3}$$

moles needed in $100\,cm^3 = 0.478 \times 0.100 = 0.0478$ mol

mass = moles × molar mass = $0.0478 \times 82 = 3.92$ g

MODE OF ACTION

- For a buffer solution to work there must be relatively large and similar concentrations of both the weak acid and its conjugate base.
- Think about a buffer solution containing a mixture of a weak acid HA and the sodium salt containing its conjugate base A^-.
- The acid is only slightly ionised:
  $HA \rightleftharpoons H^+ + A^-$
- The salt is totally ionised:
  $NaA \rightarrow Na^+ + A^-$
- This means that there are similar quantities of HA molecules and A^- ions in solution.

ADDITION OF H^+

- When a small amount of H^+ ions are added, they react with the A^- ions from the large reservoir of A^- ions from the salt:
  $H^+ + A^- \rightarrow HA$
- Because the amount of A^- was large and only a small amount of H^+ was added, $[A^-]$ remains approximately constant.
- Because the original amount of HA was large and only a small amount was produced by the reaction above, [HA] remains approximately constant.
- As both are approximately unchanged, $[H^+]$ and hence the pH are also approximately unchanged.

ADDITION OF OH^-

- When a small amount of OH^- ions are added, they react with the large reservoir of HA molecules:
  $OH^- + HA \rightarrow A^- + H_2O$
- As with addition of H^+, the relatively large values of [HA] and $[A^-]$ do not alter significantly, and so $[H^+]$ and hence pH do not alter significantly.

KEY POINTS

- Added H^+ reacts with A^- from salt.
- As the initial concentrations of HA and A^- are relatively large, [HA] and $[A^-]$ do not change significantly.
- $[H^+]$ and pH do not change significantly.

REDOX EQUILIBRIA

OXIDATION NUMBER

DEFINITION

- **The oxidation number of an element is worked out as either the actual charge on that element in an ion, or the charge it would have if the bonding electrons were given to the more electronegative element.**
- For example:
  - In sodium chloride, which consists of Na^+ and Cl^- ions, the sodium has an oxidation number of +1 and chlorine of −1.
  - In covalent hydrogen chloride, the chlorine is more electronegative than the hydrogen and two electrons are shared. The chlorine is 'given' the two, but as one belonged to the chlorine, it has a notional gain of one electron and so has an oxidation number of −1. Hydrogen 'loses' the bonding electrons, one of which was its own, so has an oxidation number of +1.
  - In CCl_4, chlorine is more electronegative than carbon, so gains the bonding electrons. Each chlorine has an oxidation number of −1.

RULES FOR EVALUATING OXIDATION NUMBERS

1. The oxidation number of an uncombined element is zero.
2. The oxidation numbers in a neutral compound add up to zero.
3. The oxidation numbers of the elements in an ion add up to the charge on that ion.
4. All Group 1 elements have an oxidation number of +1 in their compounds, and all Group 2 elements are +2 in their compounds.
5. Hydrogen is +1 in its compounds except when bonded to a metal when it is −1.
6. Fluorine is always −1 in its compounds.
7. Oxygen is always −2 in its compounds except when bonded to fluorine or in peroxides and superoxides.

WORKED EXAMPLE

Calculate the oxidation number of sulphur in
(a) S_2 (b) SO_2 (c) H_2S (d) SO_4^{2-} (e) $S_2O_3^{2-}$

(a) Zero: it is not joined to another element.
(b) +4: each oxygen is −2 (rule 7) making a total of −4. As SO_2 is neutral, the sulphur must balance this (rule 2).
(c) −2: each hydrogen is +1 (rule 5) making a total of +2. As H_2S is neutral, the sulphur must balance this (rule 2).
(d) +6: each of the four oxygen atoms is −2 (rule 7) making a total of −8, but the ion is 2−, so the sulphur, oxidation number x, and the oxygen atoms, −8, must add up to −2 (rule 3). So $x + (-8) = -2$, $x = +6$.
(e) +2: the three oxygen atoms add up to −6 (rule 7) and the ion is −2, so the oxidation numbers of the two sulphur atoms and the −6 of the three oxygen atoms must add up to −2 (rule 3). So the two sulphur atoms are +4, and each is +2.

WORKED EXAMPLE

Calculate the oxidation numbers of chromium in
(a) $Cr_2O_7^{2-}$ (b) CrO_4^{2-} (c) $Cr_2(SO_4)_3$

(a) +6: the seven oxygen atoms are −14, the ion is −2, so the two chromium atoms are +12 between them or +6 each.
(b) Also +6: the four oxygen atoms add up to −8, the ion is −2, so the chromium atom is +6.
(c) +3: the SO_4 ion is −2, so three SO_4 ions add up to −6. This is balanced by the two chromium atoms which must be +3 each.

REDOX REACTIONS

DEFINITIONS

- **Oxidation Is the Loss of electrons.**
- **It can also be defined as when the oxidation number of an element increases.**
- **Reduction Is the Gain of electrons.**
- **It can also be defined as when the oxidation number of an element decreases.**
- This can be remembered by the phrase **OILRIG**.

HALF-EQUATIONS

- Half-equations must balance for charge as well as for numbers of atoms.
- The number of electrons equals the total change of oxidation number of the element being oxidised or reduced.

Oxidation

- **Half-equations** for oxidation have electrons on the right.
- The **oxidation number** of the element being oxidised increases.
- For example:
  - The oxidation of zinc atoms, with oxidation numbers underneath, is:

    $Zn(s) \rightarrow Zn^{2+}(aq) + 2e^-$

    0   +2
  - The oxidation of hydrogen peroxide, with the oxidation numbers for oxygen underneath, is:

    $H_2O_2(aq) \rightarrow 2H^+(aq) + O_2(g) + 2e^-$

    −1 each   0

Reduction

- **Half-equations** for reduction have electrons on the left.
- The **oxidation number** of the element being reduced decreases.
- For example:
  - The reduction of silver ions, with oxidation numbers written underneath, is:

    $Ag^+(aq) + e^- \rightarrow Ag(s)$

    +1   0
- When the substance being reduced is in acid solution, H^+ ions are added to the left-hand side of the equation.
- For example:
  - The half-equation for the reduction of manganate(VII) ions in acid solution is:

    $MnO_4^-(aq) + 8H^+(aq) + 5e^- \rightarrow Mn^{2+}(aq) + 4H_2O(l)$

    +7   +2

OVERALL REDOX EQUATIONS

- Overall redox equations are obtained by adding the two half-equations
  - having first made sure that the number of electrons in the two half-equations are the same.
- For example:
  - The oxidation of zinc atoms by silver ions:
    The silver ion half-equation has to be doubled and then added to the zinc half-equation.

    $Zn(s) \rightarrow Zn^{2+}(aq) + 2e^-$

    $2Ag^+(aq) + 2e^- \rightarrow 2Ag(s)$

    $Zn(s) + 2Ag^+(aq) \rightarrow Zn^{2+}(aq) + 2Ag(s)$

    0   +1 × 2   +2   0 × 2

    down by 2

    up by 2

The change in oxidation numbers is the same. One zinc goes up by 2, two silver ions go down by 1 each.

  - The oxidation of hydrogen peroxide by acidified manganate(VII) ions:
    The hydrogen peroxide equation must be multiplied by 5.
    The manganate(VII) equation must be multiplied by 2.
    Then both equations have 10 electrons and can be added together.

    $5H_2O_2(aq) \rightarrow 10H^+(aq) + 5O_2(g) + 10e^-$

    $2MnO_4^-(aq) + 16H^+(aq) + 10e^- \rightarrow 2Mn^{2+}(aq) + 8H_2O(l)$

    $5H_2O_2(aq) + 2MnO_4^-(aq) + 6H^+(aq) \rightarrow 5O_2(g) + 2Mn^{2+}(aq) + 8H_2O(l)$

    −1 × 10   +7 × 2   0 × 10   +2 × 2

    down by 10

    up by 10

Again, the change in oxidation numbers is the same. The ten oxygen atoms in $5H_2O_2$ go up by 1 each = 10 and the two manganese in $2MnO_4^-$ go down by 5 each = 10.

MUST REMEMBER

- All electrons **must** be cancelled when getting the overall equation.
- Check too that species that appear on both sides, such as H^+ ions, also cancel.

OXIDISING AND REDUCING AGENTS

- **An oxidising agent is a substance that will oxidise another substance and so be reduced itself. It will gain electrons and/or have its oxidation number reduced.**
  - Chlorine is an oxidising agent and is reduced to the –1 oxidation state.
- **A reducing agent is a substance that will reduce other substances and becomes oxidised. It will lose electrons and its oxidation number will increase.**
  - Tin(II) ions are reducing agents and are oxidised to tin(IV) compounds, with a gain of +2 in oxidation number.

MUST REMEMBER

- Always give state symbols in redox equations and half-equations.

WORKED EXAMPLE

(a) Write the half-equations for the reduction of dichromate(VI) ions in acidic solution and for the oxidation of Fe^{2+} ions.

The dichromate(VI) ions are reduced to Cr^{3+} ions

$Cr_2O_7^{2-}(aq) + 14H^+(aq) + 6e^- \rightarrow 2Cr^{3+}(aq) + 7H_2O(l)$

$+6 \times 2$ $\quad$ $+3 \times 2$ $\quad$ total change of –6 $\quad$ (–3 for each chromium ion)

The Fe^{2+} ions are oxidised to Fe^{3+} ions

$Fe^{2+}(aq) \rightarrow Fe^{3+}(aq) + e^-$ $\quad$ total change of +1

(b) Use these to deduce the overall equation.

The oxidation half-equation of Fe^{2+} has to be multiplied by 6 and added to the dichromate(VI) equation so that the electrons cancel.

$$6Fe^{2+}(aq) \rightarrow 6Fe^{3+}(aq) + 6e^-$$
$$Cr_2O_7^{2-}(aq) + 14H^+(aq) + 6e^- \rightarrow 2Cr^{3+}(aq) + 7H_2O(l)$$
$$Cr_2O_7^{2-}(aq) + 14H^+(aq) + 6Fe^{2+}(aq) \rightarrow 2Cr^{3+}(aq) + 7H_2O(l) + 6Fe^{3+}(aq)$$

(c) State which is the oxidising agent and which the reducing agent.

The dichromate ions oxidise the Fe^{2+} ions to Fe^{3+}, so they are the oxidising agent. The Fe^{2+} ions reduce the dichromate(VI) ions to chromium(III) ions, so Fe^{2+} ions are the reducing agent.

WORKED EXAMPLE

Explain whether or not the reaction below is a redox reaction.

$$Cr_2O_7^{2-}(aq) + 2OH^-(aq) \rightarrow 2CrO_4^{2-}(aq) + H_2O(l)$$

The chromium in $Cr_2O_7^{2-}$ is in the +6 state and the chromium in CrO_4^{2-} is also in the +6 state, so it has neither been reduced nor oxidised. The reaction is not a redox reaction.

start Edexcel only

DISPROPORTIONATION REACTIONS

- **A disproportionation reaction is a reaction in which the same species is simultaneously oxidised and reduced.**
- It is a special type of redox reaction.
- To be able to be simultaneously oxidised and reduced, the element must exist in three different oxidation states.
- For example, chlorine:
  - When chlorine is added to aqueous sodium hydroxide, a disproportionation reaction takes place.
    $Cl_2(g) + 2OH^-(aq) \rightarrow Cl^-(aq) + OCl^-(aq) + H_2O(l)$
    0 −1 +1
  - The chlorine (oxidation number **0**) is simultaneously reduced to Cl^- ions (oxidation number −1) and oxidised to OCl^- ions (oxidation number +1).

MUST REMEMBER

- There can only be **one** species containing the element that disproportionates on the **left** of the equation.
- There must be **two** species containing that element on the **right**.

end Edexcel only

ELECTROCHEMICAL CELLS

- An electrochemical cell consists of two metal electrodes each dipping into an ionic solution, connected internally by a salt bridge and externally by wires.
- If the metals or the solutions are different, a potential difference is set up and an electric current will flow.
- Oxidation will take place at one electrode – the **anode**.
- Reduction will take place at the other electrode – the **cathode**.
- Electrons will flow through the external wires and ions will move through the solutions.
- For example:
  - The reaction between magnesium and hydrochloric acid can be carried out in such a way that electricity is generated.

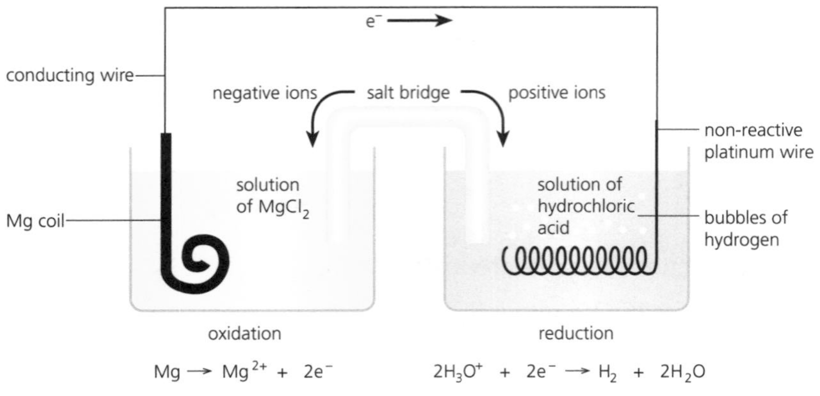

Simple electrochemical cell

MUST REMEMBER

- **O**xidation takes place at the **a**node (both **o** and **a** are vowels).
- **R**eduction takes place at the **c**athode (both **r** and **c** are consonants).

STANDARD ELECTRODE POTENTIALS, E⊖

- **The standard electrode potential is the electric potential when a metal is dipped into a solution of ions under standard conditions. It can only be measured as a potential difference when coupled to another electrode, for example.**
- The standard conditions are:
  - All solutions must be at a concentration of 1 mol dm^{-3}.
  - Any gases must be at a standard pressure of 101 kN m^{-2} (101 kPa) or 1 atm.
  - The temperature must be stated. It is usually 298K (25°C).
- Standard electrode potentials are normally written as a **reduction potential** with the electrons on the left of the equation.
- The electrode is connected, via a salt bridge, to either a standard hydrogen electrode or a reference electrode with a known electric potential.

Standard hydrogen electrode

- This consists of hydrogen gas, at 1 atm or 101 kPa pressure, bubbling over a platinum electrode immersed in a solution of 1.00 mol dm^{-3} HCl, all at a temperature of 298K.
- **A standard hydrogen electrode has a potential of 0 volts.**

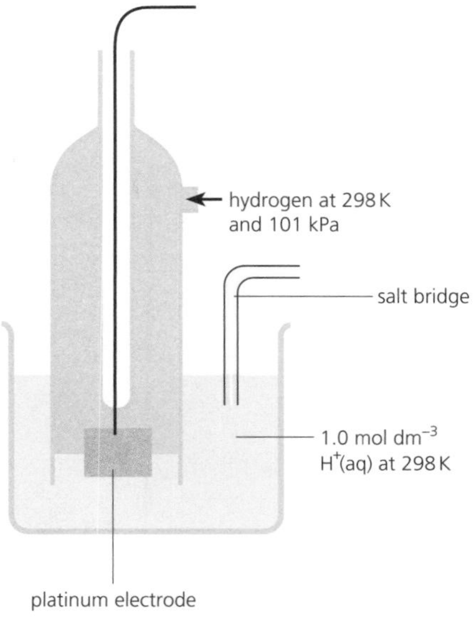

Standard hydrogen electrode

A standard metal electrode

- This consists of a rod of the metal dipping into a solution of its ions at a concentration of 1.00 mol dm^{-3} and a temperature of 298K.

A standard redox system of two ions, such as Fe^{3+}/Fe^{2+}

This consists of a platinum rod dipping into a solution that is 1.00 mol dm^{-3} in both ions, at a temperature of 298K.

A standard gaseous non-metal electrode such as chlorine

This consists of a platinum rod, over which the chlorine gas at 101 kPa (1 atm) pressure is bubbling, dipping into a 1.00 mol dm^{-3} solution of Cl^- ions, at a temperature of 298K.

USE OF A STANDARD HYDROGEN ELECTRODE TO MEASURE A STANDARD ELECTRODE POTENTIAL

- A high resistance voltmeter is connected across the two electrodes.
- A salt bridge is used to complete the circuit.

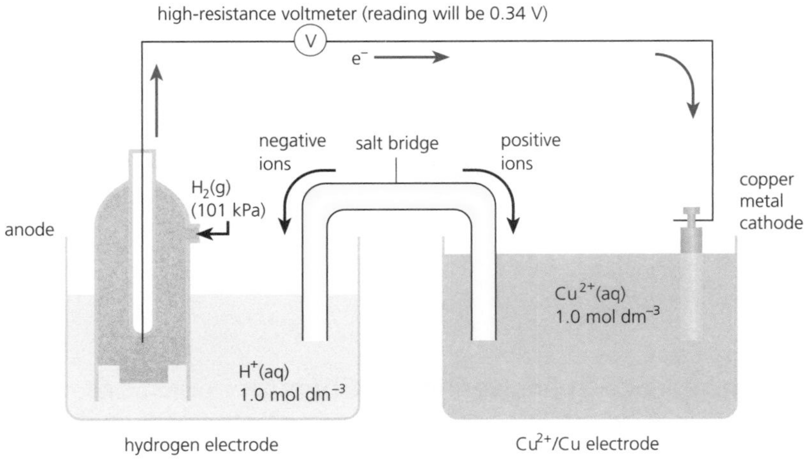

RELATIVE POWERS AS OXIDISING OR REDUCING AGENTS

It is normal to list standard electrode potentials in increasing order with the most negative at the top and the most positive at the bottom.

Reduction half-equation	$E^\ominus$ / V	
$Li^+(aq) + e^- \rightarrow Li(s)$	−3.40	
$Mg^{2+}(aq) + 2e^- \rightarrow Mg(s)$	−2.37	
$Zn^{2+}(aq) + 2e^- \rightarrow Zn(s)$	−0.76	
$Fe^{2+}(aq) + 2e^- \rightarrow Fe(s)$	−0.44	
$2H^+(aq) + 2e^- \rightarrow H_2(g)$	0	
$Cu^{2+} + 2e^- \rightarrow Cu(s)$	+0.34	increasing power as an oxidising agent (↓)
$O_2(g) + 2H_2O(l) + 4e^- \rightarrow 4OH^-(aq)$	+0.40	
$I_2(aq) + 2e^- \rightarrow 2I^-(aq)$	+0.54	
$Fe^{3+}(aq) + e^- \rightarrow Fe^{2+}(aq)$	+0.77	
$Cr_2O_7^{2-}(aq) + 14H^+(aq) + 6e^- \rightarrow 2Cr^{3+}(aq) + 7H_2O(l)$	+1.33	
$Cl_2(g) + 2e^- \rightarrow 2Cl^-(aq)$	+1.36	
$MnO_4^-(aq) + 8H^+(aq) + 5e^- \rightarrow Mn^{2+}(aq) + 4H_2O(l)$	+1.51	

- In an equation, the substance on the left with the smaller negative (or larger positive) $E^\ominus$ value is the easier to reduce. This means that it is a stronger oxidising agent than the substance on the left with a more negative (or less positive) $E^\ominus$ value.
- For example:
  - Cu^{2+} ions will oxidise Zn atoms because the value of $E^\ominus$ for Cu^{2+}/Cu is more positive than the $E^\ominus$ for Zn^{2+}/Zn.
- The best oxidising agents are the substances on the left of the half-equations with the largest positive $E^\ominus$ values. Manganate(VII) ions are strong oxidising agents.
- The best reducing agents are the substances on the right of the half-equations with the largest negative $E^\ominus$ values. Lithium metal is a powerful reducing agent.

MUST TAKE CARE

- If the equation is doubled or halved, the electrode potential does **not** alter.
- For example:

$$O_2(g) + 2H_2O(l) + 4e^- \rightarrow 4OH^-(aq) \qquad E^\ominus = +0.40\ V$$

and

$$\tfrac{1}{2}O_2(g) + H_2O(l) + 2e^- \rightarrow 2OH^-(aq) \qquad E^\ominus = +0.40\ V$$

CALCULATING THE VALUE OF $E^\ominus_{cell}$ AND HENCE PREDICTING LIKELIHOOD OF REACTION

- The value of the cell potential, $E^\ominus_{cell}$, can be worked out from standard electrode potential data.
- For the question 'Will substance A oxidise substance B?' the data is:

  $A + e^- \rightarrow X$ $\quad E^\ominus = p$ volts

  $Y + e^- \rightarrow B$ $\quad E^\ominus = q$ volts
- Note that the substance to be oxidised, B, is currently on the right of the given reduction half-equations.
- First write down the half-equation for the reduction of A and then the half-equation for the oxidation of B.
- The $E^\ominus$ value for the half-equation involving B must have its sign reversed, because the half-equation has been reversed.

  $A + e^- \rightarrow X$ $\quad E^\ominus = p$ volts

  $B \rightarrow Y + e^-$ $\quad E^\ominus = -q$ volts
- The overall equation is the sum of these two, and the $E^\ominus_{cell}$ is the sum of these two $E^\ominus$ values.

  $A + B \rightarrow X + Y$ $\quad E^\ominus_{cell} = p + (-q)$ volts

MUST REMEMBER

- If the value of $E^\ominus_{cell}$ is **positive**, the reaction will proceed from **left to right**.
- If the value of $E^\ominus_{cell}$ is **negative**, the reaction will proceed in the reverse direction – from **right to left**.

WORKED EXAMPLE

Using the data in the table on the previous page, work out whether chloride ions will be oxidised by dichromate(VI) ions in acidic solution.

The reactants are Cl^- and $Cr_2O_7^{2-}$ and so both must be on the **left** of the half-equations, so the Cl_2/Cl^- half-equation must be reversed.

$2Cl^-(aq) \rightarrow Cl_2(g) + 2e^-$ $\quad E^\ominus = -(+1.36)\text{ V} = -1.36\text{ V}$

$Cr_2O_7^{2-}(aq) + 14H^+(aq) + 6e^- \rightarrow 2Cr^{3+}(aq) + 7H_2O(l)$ $\quad E^\ominus = +1.33\text{ V}$

$E^\ominus_{cell} = -1.36 + 1.33 = -0.03$ V which is negative, so dichromate(VI) ions will not oxidise chloride ions under standard conditions.

A negative $E^\ominus_{cell}$ value shows that the reaction will not take place under standard conditions. However, concentrated solutions of potassium dichromate(VI) will oxidise concentrated hydrochloric acid because the conditions are not standard.

WORKED EXAMPLE

Using the data in the table on the previous page, work out whether iodide ions will reduce Fe^{3+} ions to Fe^{2+} ions.

The reactants are I^- ions and Fe^{3+} ions, so the I_2/I^- half-equation must be reversed and the sign of its $E^\ominus$ value changed.

$2I^-(aq) \rightarrow I_2(s) + 2e^-$ $\quad E^\ominus = -(+0.54) = -0.54$ V

$Fe^{3+}(aq) + e^- \rightarrow Fe^{2+}(aq)$ $\quad E^\ominus = +0.77$ V

$E^\ominus_{cell} = -0.54 + 0.77 = +0.23$V

This is positive, so iodide ions should reduce iron(III) ions to iron(II) ions.

A positive $E^\ominus_{cell}$ value does not prove that the reaction will take place at room temperature. The reaction may be too slow to observe due to a high activation energy.

start

AQA only

CELL CONVENTION

- There is a convention that is simpler than drawing cells.
  - The anode (where oxidation takes place) is written on the left.
  - The cathode (where reduction takes place) is written on the right.
  - The chemicals are written in the order: reactant before product.
  - A single vertical line separates substances which are in different phases.
  - A double line represents the salt bridge.
- For example:
  - The cell convention for the cell shown below is:

    $Pt(s) \mid H_2(g) \mid H^+(aq) \parallel Cu^{2+}(aq) \mid Cu(s)$
  - The equation is:

    $H_2(g) + Cu^{2+}(aq) \rightarrow 2H^+(aq) + Cu(s)$

    $E^\ominus_{cell}$ is given by $E^\ominus_{right\ electrode} - E^\ominus_{left\ electrode} = (+0.34) - (0) = +0.34\ V$

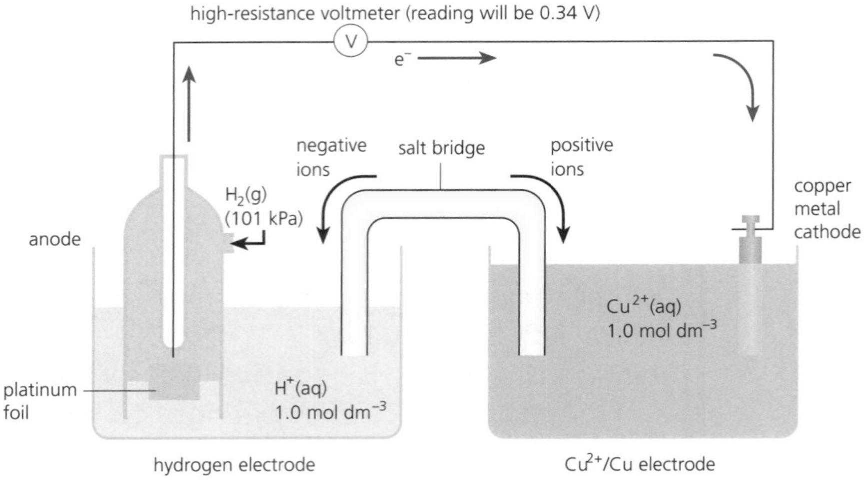

WORKED EXAMPLE

Draw the cell convention for the oxidation of iron(II) ions by manganate(VII) ions in acid solution and calculate the standard cell potential.

The Fe^{2+} ions are oxidised and so go on the left.

$Pt \mid Fe^{2+}, Fe^{3+} \parallel MnO_4^-, H^+, Mn^{2+}, H_2O \mid Pt$

$E^\ominus_{cell} = E^\ominus_{right\ electrode} - E^\ominus_{left\ electrode} = E^\ominus(MnO_4^-/Mn^{2+}) - E^\ominus(Fe^{3+}/Fe^{2+})$

$= (+1.51) - (+0.77)$

$= +0.74\ V$

The value of $E^\ominus_{cell}$ has the $E^\ominus$ of the left electrode subtracted because the half-equation for what happens at the anode has to be reversed.

end

AQA only

CORROSION

- OCR does not require E values to be discussed, but may ask for the equations involved in rusting and the methods of prevention.

- Iron rusts when in the presence of oxygen and water. The process is a redox reaction which occurs via an electrochemical cell.
- The standard electrode potentials for the two species are:
  $Fe^{2+}(aq) + 2e^- \rightarrow Fe(s)$ $E^\ominus = -0.44$ V
  $\frac{1}{2}O_2(g) + H_2O(l) + 2e^- \rightarrow 2OH^-(aq)$ $E^\ominus = +0.40$ V
- Iron atoms lose electrons which flow through the metal and reach oxygen dissolved in the water.
- The two half-equations for the reactions in rusting are:
  $Fe(s) \rightarrow Fe^{2+}(aq) + 2e^-$ $E = -(-0.44) = +0.44$ V (approx)
  $\frac{1}{2}O_2(aq) + H_2O(l) + 2e^- \rightarrow 2OH^-(aq)$ $E = +0.40$ V (approx)
- The overall reaction and the value of E_{cell} are obtained by adding these two half-equations.
  $Fe(s) + \frac{1}{2}O_2(aq) + H_2O(l) \rightarrow Fe(OH)_2(s)$ $E_{cell} = (+0.44) + (+0.40) = 0.84$ V (approx)
- The iron(II) hydroxide is then oxidised to hydrated iron(III) oxide by the oxygen in the air. This is the red rust that is seen on iron exposed to air and water.

- The E values are not standard values because:
  - the oxygen is dissolved not gaseous
  - the iron(II) hydroxide precipitates
  - the solutions are not 1 mol dm^{-3}.

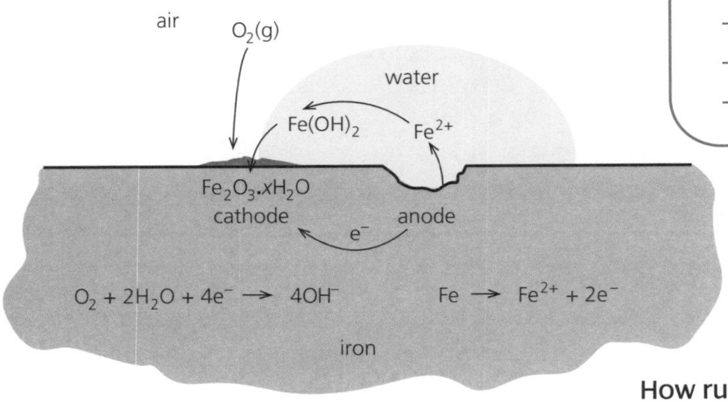

How rusting occurs

PREVENTION OF CORROSION

The three common ways are:

1. Coating the iron with paint or another physical barrier
   This not only prevents the dissolved oxygen reaching the iron but also forms a non-conducting barrier so that the electrons cannot move from the iron to the dissolved oxygen.
2. Coating the iron with a layer of a more reactive metal such as zinc – **galvanising**
   As the Zn^{2+}/Zn electrode potential is more negative than that of Fe^{2+}/Fe, zinc is more readily oxidised than iron. This means that the layer of zinc slowly corrodes rather than the iron.
3. Using an alloy of iron and chromium (stainless steel)
   The chromium forms a protective layer of chromium(III) oxide over the surface of the metal. If scratched, a new protective layer forms.

ESTIMATION OF A REDUCING AGENT

- A **reducing agent** can be titrated against a standard solution of potassium manganate(VII) in the presence of dilute sulphuric acid.
- The method is:
  - Pipette a 25.0 cm^3 sample of the reducing agent into a conical flask.
  - Add approximately 25 cm^3 of dilute sulphuric acid.
  - Fill a burette with standard potassium manganate(VII) solution and slowly run it into the conical flask until the solution just stays pale pink.
  - Repeat the titration until two consistent titres are obtained.
  - Write the overall equation for the reaction.
  - Calculate the moles of reducing agent in the 25.0 cm^3 sample using:

$$\text{moles of reducing agent} = \text{moles } KMnO_4 \text{ in titre} \times \frac{\text{moles of reducing agent in equation}}{\text{moles of } KMnO_4 \text{ in equation}}$$

WORKED EXAMPLE

A sample of hydrated iron(II) sulphate, $FeSO_4.xH_2O$, of mass 8.23 g was dissolved in water and made up to a volume of 250 cm^3. 25.0 cm^3 portions of this were titrated against 0.0250 mol dm^{-3} potassium manganate(VII) solution. The mean titre was 23.7 cm^3. Calculate the value of *x* in the formula for the hydrated iron(II) sulphate. The equation is:

$$5Fe^{2+} + MnO_4^- + 8H^+ \rightarrow 5Fe^{3+} + Mn^{2+} + 4H_2O$$

Amount of MnO_4^- in titre $= 0.0237 \times 0.0250 = 5.925 \times 10^{-4}$ mol
Amount of Fe^{2+} in 25.0 cm^3 $= 5 \times 5.925 \times 10^{-4} = 0.002\,96$ mol
Amount of Fe^{2+} in 250 cm^3 $= 10 \times 0.002\,96 = 0.0296$ mol
Molar mass of $FeSO_4.xH_2O$ $= 8.23 / 0.0296 = 278$ g mol^{-1}
Mass of H_2O in $FeSO_4.xH_2O$ $= 278 - (56 + 32 + 4 \times 16) = 126$
x = moles of water = 126 / 18 = 7

ESTIMATION OF AN OXIDISING AGENT

- The **oxidising agent** is added to excess potassium iodide solution (sometimes in the presence of dilute sulphuric acid) and the liberated iodine is titrated with standard sodium thiosulphate solution, $Na_2S_2O_3(aq)$.
- The method is:
  - Pipette a 25.0 cm^3 sample of the oxidising agent into a conical flask.
  - Add approximately 25 cm^3 of potassium iodide solution (an excess).
  - Fill a burette with standard sodium thiosulphate solution and slowly run it in until the iodine colour fades to a pale straw colour.
  - Add a few drops of starch indicator and continue until the blue-black colour disappears.
  - Repeat until two consistent titres are obtained.
- The equation for the reaction between sodium thiosulphate and iodine is:
  $2Na_2S_2O_3 + I_2 \rightarrow 2NaI + Na_2S_4O_6$
- The number of moles of I_2 produced by oxidising agent $= \frac{1}{2} \times$ moles of $Na_2S_2O_3$ in titre.

WORKED EXAMPLE

25.0 cm^3 portions of a solution of domestic bleach, containing NaOCl, were added to excess acidified potassium iodide and the liberated iodine titrated against a 0.111 mol dm^{-3} solution of sodium thiosulphate. The mean titre was 27.4 cm^3. Calculate the concentration of NaOCl in the bleach. The equations are:

$$NaOCl + 2I^- + 2H^+ \rightarrow NaCl + I_2 + H_2O$$
$$2Na_2S_2O_3 + I_2 \rightarrow 2NaI + Na_2S_4O_6$$

Amount of sodium thiosulphate
$= 0.0274 \times 0.111 = 0.003\,04$ mol
1 mol of $Na_2S_2O_3$ reacts with $\frac{1}{2}$ mol I_2
Amount of iodine liberated
$= \frac{1}{2} \times 0.003\,04 = 0.001\,52$ mol
1 mol I_2 is produced by 1 mol NaOCl
Amount of NaOCl in 25.0 cm^3 = 0.001 52 mol
Concentration of NaOCl solution
$= 0.001\,52 / 0.0250 = 0.0608$ mol dm^{-3}

AS KINETICS – A SUMMARY

This topic is often used for synoptic assessment and so knowledge of AS kinetics is essential.

COLLISION THEORY

- The reactant molecules must collide.
- They must collide with the correct orientation.
- They must collide with enough energy so that the collision results in reaction – this energy is called the **activation energy**, and is given the symbol E_a.

MAXWELL–BOLTZMANN DISTRIBUTION OF ENERGIES

- The molecules in a gas or in a liquid are moving around with a variety of speeds and hence kinetic energies – as shown in this figure.

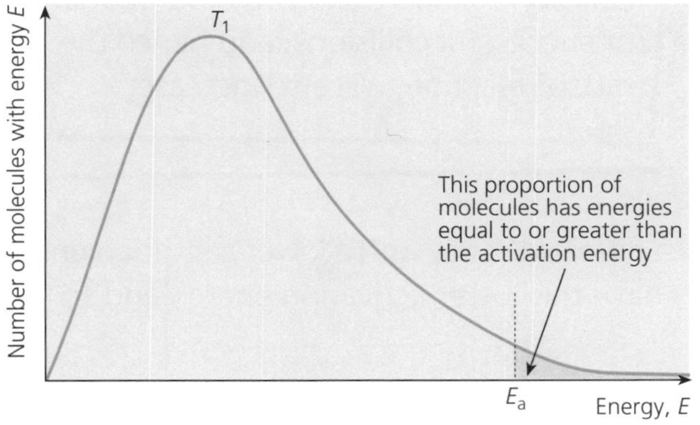

Maxwell–Boltzmann distribution curve at a temperature T_1

- If the temperature is increased, the molecules gain kinetic energy. The graph becomes 'pulled' to the right as shown in this figure.

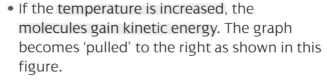

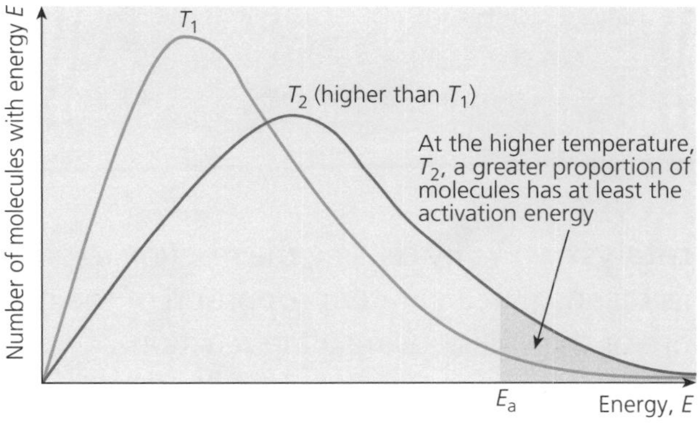

Maxwell–Boltzmann distribution curve at temperatures T_1 and T_2

MUST REMEMBER

- The graph starts at the origin and ends getting close to the x-axis – it must not cut the axis.
- It is not a bell-shaped curve, but is skewed to the right.
- **The number of molecules with energy ≥ E_a is given by the area under the curve to the right of the E_a value.**

MUST REMEMBER

- The peak of the higher temperature graph is lower and further to the right.
- **The area under the curve to the right of the E_a value is greater for the higher temperature** than the lower temperature.
- The E_a values must be well to the right of the peaks.

FACTORS WHICH AFFECT RATE OF REACTION

TEMPERATURE

- When the temperature is increased, the molecules move faster so the frequency of collisions increases slightly.
  For example, if the temperature is raised by 10°C, the rate of reaction will increase by a very small amount due to the increased frequency of collisions.
- When the temperature is increased, the molecules also gain kinetic energy. This means that the proportion of the colliding molecules with energy ≥ E_a is increased – as shown by the larger shaded area to the right of E_a under the T_2 graph. This means that a larger proportion of the collisions result in reaction so the rate of reaction is increased.
  For example, if the temperature is raised by 10°C, the rate of reaction will approximately double so increased kinetic energy is the major cause of the increased rate.

MUST TAKE CARE

Don't use phrases like 'there are more collisions' or 'there are more successful collisions' because these are not precise enough.

PARTICLE SIZE FOR SOLID REACTANTS

- Solids can only react at their surface. Powders have a larger surface area than lumps, and so a powdered reactant will react faster than one in large lumps.

CONCENTRATION OF REACTANTS IN SOLUTION

- An increase in concentration causes the reactant molecules to be closer together which will increase the frequency of collision and hence the rate of reaction.

PRESSURE OF GASEOUS REACTANTS

- An increase in pressure causes the molecules to be closer together. The same proportion of the collisions will have energy ≥ E_a but the frequency of collision will increase. Thus the frequency of successful collisions, and hence the rate of reaction, will also increase.

CATALYST

- A **catalyst** works by causing the reaction to proceed by a different route with a lower activation energy.
- This means that a greater proportion of the molecules have this lower activation energy and so more of the collisions result in reaction.

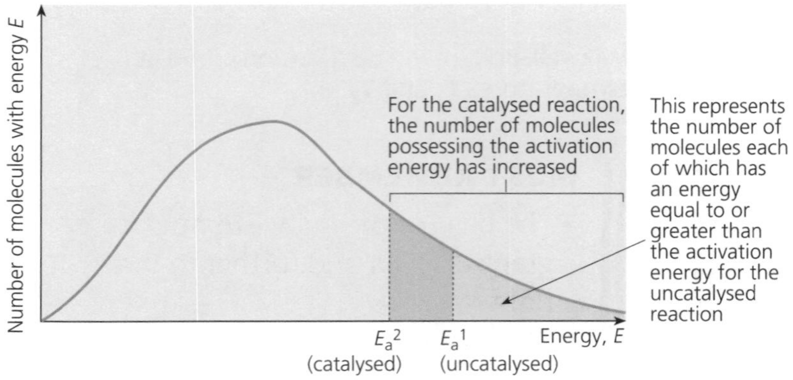

Maxwell–Boltzmann distribution showing the effect of using a catalyst

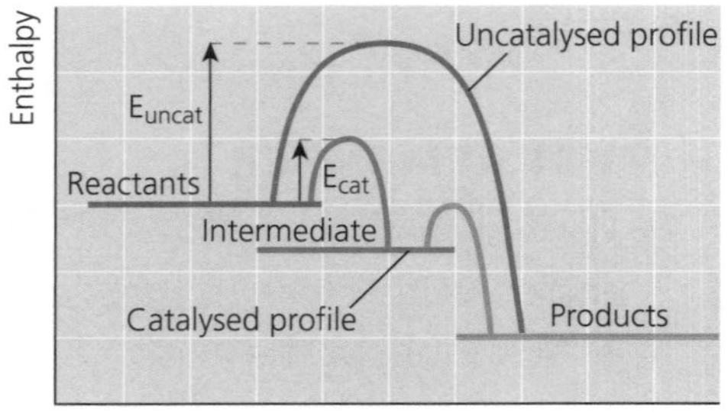

Energy profile for uncatalysed and catalysed reactions

MUST REMEMBER

- Effect of temperature: 2 curves and 1 activation energy
- Effect of catalyst: 1 curve and 2 activation energies

A2 KINETICS

RATE OF REACTION

- **Rate of reaction** is measured by the change of the concentration of a reactant or product per unit of time (normally per second).
- Its units are mol dm^{-3} s^{-1}.

RATE EQUATION

Consider a reaction
$pA + qB + rC \rightarrow$ products
It is found **experimentally** that
Rate of reaction = $k\,[A]^x\,[B]^y\,[C]^z$

- *p*, *q* and *r* are the stoichiometric numbers in the chemical equation.

- *x*, *y* and *z* are the powers to which the concentrations are raised in the rate equation.
- The numbers *x*, *y* and *z* may or may not equal *p*, *q* and *r*.

ORDER

- **The order of the reaction is the sum of the powers to which the concentrations of the reactants (and any catalyst) are raised in the experimentally-determined rate equation.**
- In the example above, the order of the reaction $= x + y + z$.

PARTIAL ORDER

- **The partial order of one reactant (or the order with respect to one reactant) is the power to which its concentration is raised in the experimentally-determined rate equation.**
- In the example above the partial order of A is *x*.
- If the concentration of a reactant does not affect the rate of reaction, it will not appear in the rate equation – it therefore has a zero partial order.

RATE CONSTANT

- **The rate constant, *k*, is the constant in the rate equation which connects the rate of reaction with the concentrations of the reactants.**
- Its units depend on the order of the reaction.
- Reactions with small value of *k* will be slower than those with a large value, if the concentrations of the reactants are the same.

ORDER OF REACTION AND MECHANISM

- The order of reaction depends on the mechanism of the reaction and cannot be predicted from the stoichiometry of the chemical equation.
- Most reactions take place in more than one step – the slowest step is called the **rate-determining step (r.d.s.)**.
- Consider the hydrolysis of a tertiary halogenoalkane:
  $(CH_3)_3CBr + OH^- \rightarrow (CH_3)_3COH + Br^-$
  – The rate equation, found by experiment, is rate $= k\,[(CH_3)_3CBr]^1$
  – As $[OH^-]$ does not appear in the rate equation, OH^- ions must enter the mechanism after the rate-determining step – the reaction is said to be zero order with respect to OH^- ions.
  – This agrees with the following mechanism:

$$(CH_3)_3CBr \xrightarrow{\text{slower}} (CH_3)_3C^+ + Br^-$$

$$(CH_3)_3C^+ + OH^- \xrightarrow{\text{faster}} (CH_3)_3COH$$

  – Here, the first step is the rate-determining step.

WORKED EXAMPLE

The iodination, in acid solution, of propanone

$$CH_3COCH_3 + I_2 \xrightarrow{H^+(cat)} CH_3COCH_2I + HI$$

has the following rate equation: rate = k $[CH_3COCH_3][H^+]$

Show that this is consistent with the following mechanism.

Step 1 (slow): $CH_3COCH_3 + H^+ \rightarrow CH_3C^+(OH)CH_3 \rightarrow CH_3C(OH){=}CH_2 + H^+$

Step 3 (fast): $CH_3C(OH){=}CH_2 + I_2 \rightarrow CH_3C^+(OH)CH_2I + I^-$

Step 4 (fast): $CH_3C^+(OH)CH_2I \rightarrow CH_3COCH_2I + H^+$

As the orders of CH_3COCH_3 and H^+ are both 1, one of each must be in the mechanism up to and including the rate-determining step. This is in agreement with the mechanism, where one of each is in step 1 which is the rate-determining step.

As the order with respect to iodine is zero, it must enter the mechanism **after** the rate-determining step. It appears in step 2, which is after the rate-determining step.

FACTORS AFFECTING RATE CONSTANT, *k*

ACTIVATION ENERGY, E_a

- A small value of E_a will result in a large value of k and so a fast reaction.
- Catalysts cause the reaction to go via a different mechanism, and the activation energy of the new rate-determining step is less than that of the uncatalysed rate-determining step. This means that the rate equation for the catalysed reaction has a larger value of k so the rate is faster.

TEMPERATURE

- An increase in the temperature will cause an increase in the value of k and so an increase in the rate of the reaction.

USE OF EXPERIMENTAL DATA

METHODS OF DETERMINING ORDER

Initial rates

- **The initial rate of reaction is the rate of reaction when the reactants are mixed and before their concentrations have decreased significantly.**
- It can be found by measuring the concentration change over a small interval of time.
- The initial rates can be found at different starting concentrations by doing a series of experiments. The data can then be used to find the partial orders of all the reactants, the rate equation and the value of the rate constant.

How to use initial rates

Consider the reaction: A + 3B + C → D + E

Experiment	[A] / $mol\ dm^{-3}$	[B] / $mol\ dm^{-3}$	[C] / $mol\ dm^{-3}$	Initial rate / $mol\ dm^{-3}\ s^{-1}$
1	0.10	0.10	0.10	1.0×10^{-4}
2	0.20	0.10	0.10	2.0×10^{-4}
3	0.20	0.20	0.10	8.0×10^{-4}
4	0.20	0.10	0.20	2.0×10^{-4}

The partial orders can be calculated by looking for a pair of experiments where, if possible, the concentration of only one reactant has changed.

- Consider experiments 1 and 2:
  - [A] has doubled but [B] and [C] have remained constant.
  - The rate has gone up by a factor of 2^1, so the order with respect to A is 1.
- Consider experiments 2 and 3:
  - [B] has doubled, but [A] and [C] have remained constant.
  - The rate has gone up by a factor of 4 or 2^2, so the order with respect to B is 2.
- Consider experiments 1 and 4:
  - [A] and [C] have both doubled, but [B] is constant.
  - The rate has gone up by a factor of 2^1. This would have been caused by doubling [A], and so doubling [C] has had no effect on the rate. Thus the order with respect to C is zero.

The rate equation is: rate = $k\,[A]^1\,[B]^2$

Using the data from experiment 1:

$$k = \frac{\text{rate}}{[A]\,[B]^2} = \frac{1.0 \times 10^{-4}}{(0.10) \times (0.10)^2} = 0.10\ \text{mol}^{-2}\ \text{dm}^6\ \text{s}^{-1}$$

WORKED EXAMPLE

Bromide ions can be oxidised by bromate(V) ions in acid solution.

$5Br^-(aq) + BrO_3^-(aq) + 6H^+(aq) \rightarrow 3Br_2(aq) + 3H_2O(l)$

(a) Use the data below to deduce the order with respect to Br^- ions, BrO_3^- ions and H^+ ions. You must show your reasoning.

Experiment	$[Br^-]$ / mol dm^{-3}	$[BrO_3^-]$ / mol dm^{-3}	$[H^+]$ / mol dm^{-3}	Initial rate / mol dm^{-3} s^{-1}
1	0.15	0.15	0.15	2.6×10^{-3}
2	0.15	0.30	0.15	5.2×10^{-3}
3	0.45	0.15	0.15	7.8×10^{-3}
4	0.15	0.30	0.30	20.8×10^{-3}

Consider experiments 1 and 2: $[BrO_3^-]$ increases by a factor of 2^1 and the other concentrations stay the same. The rate also increases by a factor of 2^1, so the order with respect to BrO_3^- ions is 1.
Consider experiments 1 and 3: $[Br^-]$ increases by a factor of 3^1 and the other concentrations stay the same. The rate also increases by a factor of 3^1, so the order with respect to Br^- ions is 1.
Consider experiments 2 and 4: $[H^+]$ increases by a factor of 2^1 and the other concentrations stay the same. The rate increases by a factor of 2^2, so the order with respect to H^+ ions is 2.

(b) Use your answer from (a) to deduce the rate equation and calculate the value of the rate constant, using the data from experiment 1.

The rate equation is: rate = $k\,[BrO_3^-] \times [Br^-] \times [H^+]^2$

The rate constant $k = \dfrac{\text{rate}}{[BrO_3^-] \times [Br^-] \times [H^+]^2} = \dfrac{2.6 \times 10^{-3}}{(0.15) \times (0.15) \times (0.15)^2}$

$= 5.1\ \text{mol}^{-3}\ \text{dm}^9\ \text{s}^{-1}$

The units can be calculated by the method of dimensions that was used in evaluating the units of the equilibrium constant (see page 15).

$$k = \frac{\text{concentration} \times \text{time}^{-1}}{\text{concentration}^4}$$
$= \text{concentration}^{-3} \times \text{time}^{-1}$
$= \text{mol}^{-3}\ \text{dm}^{+9}\ \text{s}^{-1}$

not AQA

CONCENTRATION/TIME GRAPHS

There are two ways of using this type of graph:

1. Use the concentration/time graph to calculate two or more half-lives.
2. Use the graph to measure the gradient (slope) at two points.

1. Calculating two or more half-lives

The half-life, $t_{1/2}$, is the time taken for the concentration of a reactant to halve.

For a **first order** reaction, the half-life is constant (within experimental error) regardless of the starting concentration.

For example:

- Hydrogen peroxide decomposes according to the equation:
  $2H_2O_2(aq) \rightarrow 2H_2O(l) + O_2(g)$
- The graph of $[H_2O_2]$ against time is shown below.
- The half-lives going from $[H_2O_2] = 0.6$ to 0.3, from 0.3 to 0.15, from 0.15 to 0.075 and from 0.075 to 0.0375 were measured.
- All were constant at 20 minutes so the reaction is first order.

The rate equation is: rate = $k\,[H_2O_2]$.

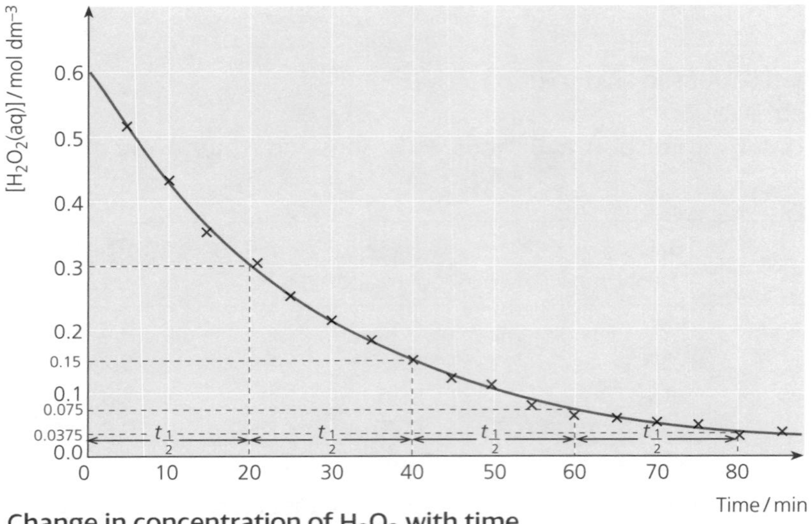

Change in concentration of H_2O_2 with time

- If a reaction such as:
  $RI + OH^- \rightarrow ROH + I^-$
  where R is an organic residue, has a constant half-life, the reaction is 1st order. This means that the rate equation is either:
  rate = k [RI] or rate = k $[OH^-]$
- To determine which equation is correct, the reaction would have to be repeated with double the concentration of OH^- ion. The slopes of the two concentration/time graphs could then be compared.
  - If the graphs were the same, the reaction would be zero order with respect to OH^- ions and 1st order in RI.
  - If the second graph was steeper, then the reaction would be 1st order with respect to OH^- ions and zero in RI.
- For the reaction given, the former is correct – the reaction is zero order with respect to OH^- ions and 1st order in RI.

2. Measuring the gradient (slope) at two points

This is difficult to do.

- Draw a tangent at the chosen concentration, and calculate the gradient of the tangent. The value of the gradient is equal to the rate of reaction at that concentration.
- Repeat this and compare the change of rate with the change in concentration.
- If both double, for example, the reaction is first order.

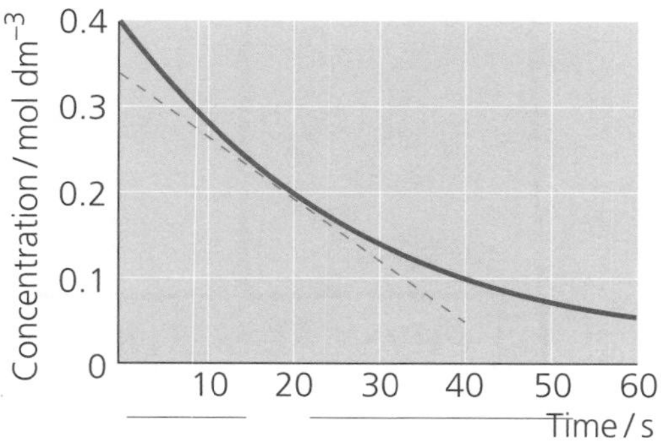

slope of tangent = $\frac{0.34 - 0.05}{40} = 0.0073$

Rate when concentration is 0.20 mol dm^{-3} = 0.0073 mol dm^{-3} s^{-1}

Measuring the gradient of a tangent to a concentration/time graph

- If a reaction

  $2A + 2B \rightarrow C + D$

  is found to be a 2nd order reaction, any one of the three rate equations could be correct:

  1. rate = k [A] × [B]
  2. rate = k [A]^2
  3. rate = k [B]^2
- Repeating the experiment with double the concentration of A would solve the problem.
  - If the rate doubled, the first equation would be correct.
  - If the rate increased by a factor of 2^2, the second equation would be correct.
  - If the rate did not alter, the third equation would be correct.

RATE/CONCENTRATION GRAPHS

- If the graph is a horizontal straight line, the reaction is zero order.
- If the graph goes up so that the rate increases by a factor of 2^1 as the concentration doubles, the reaction is 1st order.
- If the graph goes up so that the rate increases by a factor of 4 or 2^2 as the concentration doubles, the reaction is 2nd order.

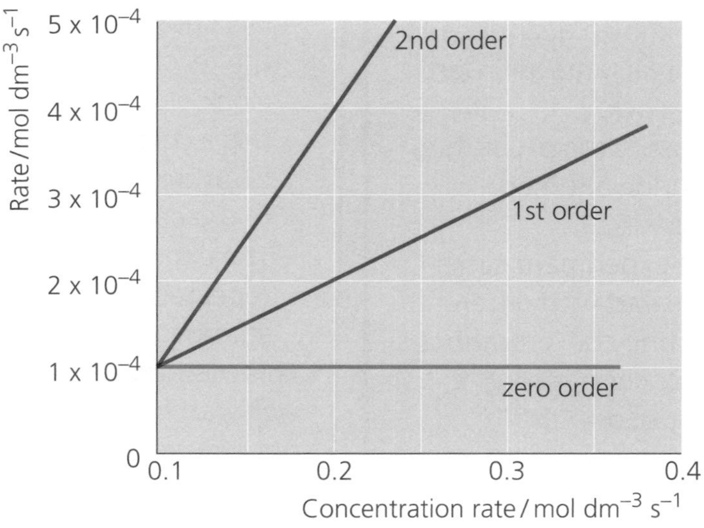

Rate/concentration graphs for zero, 1st and 2nd order reactions

end

not AQA

METHODS OF FOLLOWING A REACTION

start Edexcel only

TITRATION

- This method can be used if a reactant or a product is an acid, an alkali or iodine.
  - Mix known quantities of the reactants and start the clock.
  - At timed intervals, withdraw a portion of the reaction mixture and quench the reaction by adding some ice-cold water – this slows the reaction down, so that the reaction does not use up any more reactant, or produce any more product, during the titration.
  - Titrate the acid against a standard solution of alkali, or the alkali against a standard acid solution, or iodine against a standard solution of sodium thiosulphate.
  - Repeat until a series of readings has been obtained.
  - The experiments should all be carried out at a constant temperature.
- The burette volume is proportional to the concentration of the substance being titrated.

PHYSICAL METHODS

- The physical property can be constantly monitored and thus the need for quenching is avoided.

pH

- If an acid or an alkali is a reactant or product, the reaction can be followed using a pH meter.
  - Mix known quantities of the reactants and start the clock.
  - Measure the pH of the solution at timed intervals.
  - The experiment can be repeated with different starting concentrations.
- The concentration of a strong acid = 10^{-pH}.

Colour

- The intensity of the colour of a reactant or product depends on its concentration.
  - Mix known quantities of the reactants and start the clock.
  - Use a colorimeter to measure the concentration of the coloured substance.
  - The experiment can be repeated with different starting concentrations.
- This method would work well with iodine or potassium manganate(VII) as a reactant.

Gas volume or mass lost

- If a reaction produces a gas, by measuring either the volume of gaseous product at timed intervals or the mass at the beginning and at timed intervals, the progress of the reaction can be followed.
- The gas produced can be collected over water in a graduated tube and its volume measured.
- The mass change can be found by carrying out the experiment in a beaker standing on a top-pan balance.

end Edexcel only

STRUCTURAL ISOMERISM

CARBON CHAIN

- The **isomers** have different chain lengths.
- Only applies if there are more than three carbon atoms in the molecule.

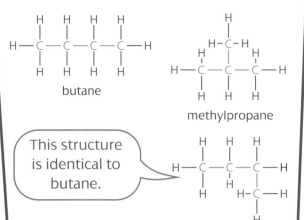

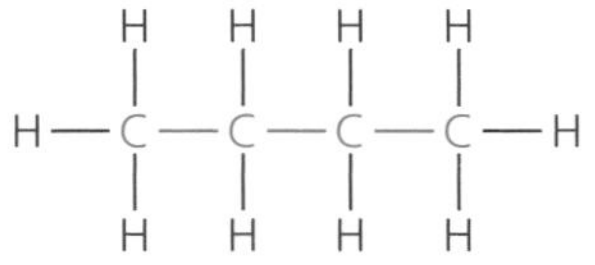
butane

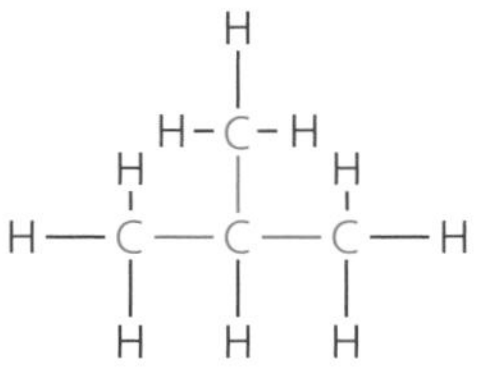
methylpropane

This structure is identical to butane.

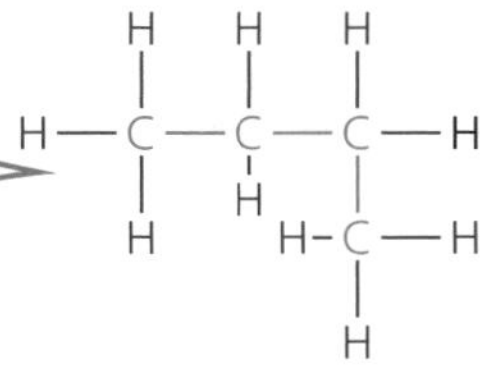

POSITIONAL

- Caused by a substituent or a functional group being in different places on the carbon chain.

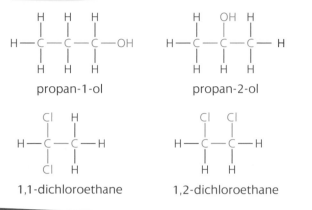

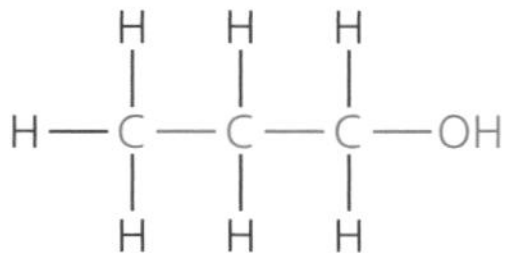
propan-1-ol

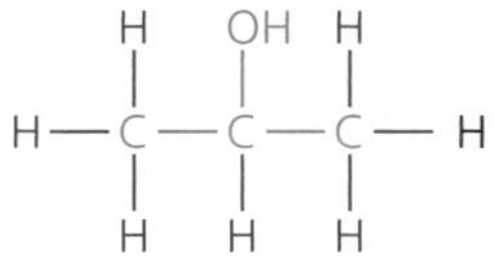
propan-2-ol

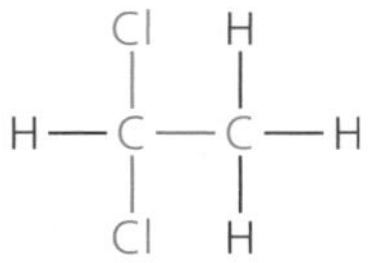
1,1-dichloroethane

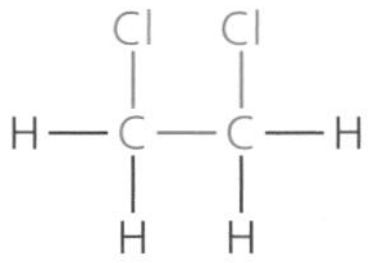
1,2-dichloroethane

Structural isomers have the same molecular formula but different structural formulae.

FUNCTIONAL GROUP ISOMERISM

- The two isomers have different functional groups:

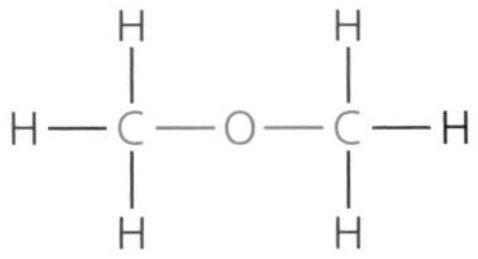
methoxymethane (an ether)

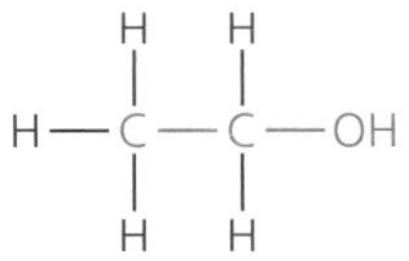
ethanol (an alcohol)

WORKED EXAMPLE

Draw all the structural isomers of C_4H_9Cl.

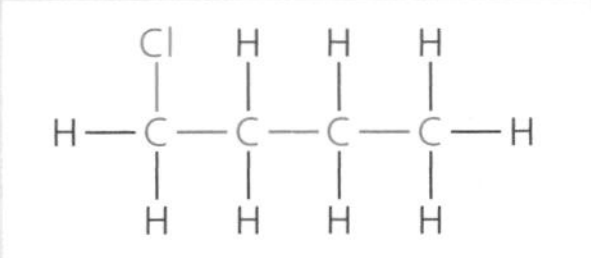
1-chlorobutane

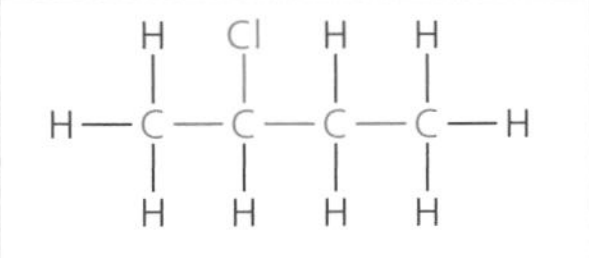
2-chlorobutane

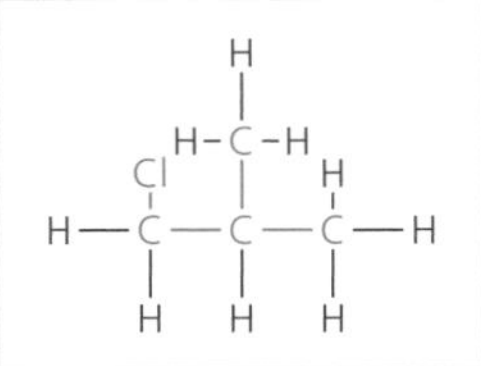
1-chloro,2-methylpropane

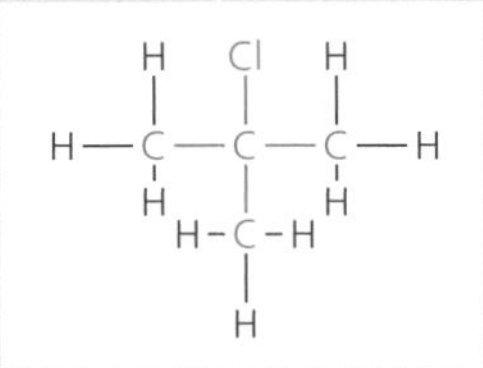
2-chloro,2-methylpropane

WORKED EXAMPLE

Draw the isomers of C_3H_6O which are alcohols or carbonyl compounds.

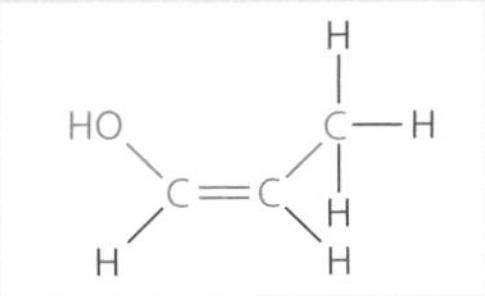
prop-1-ene-1-ol

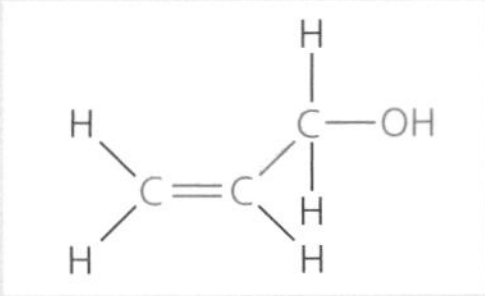
prop-2-ene-1-ol

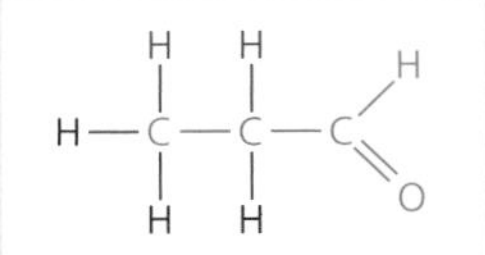
propanal

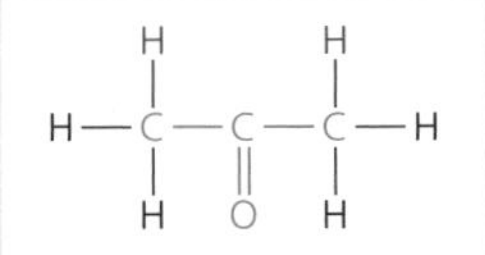
propanone

STEREOISOMERISM

GEOMETRIC ISOMERISM

Conditions for **geometric isomerism**:

- A C=C group:
  - π bond prevents rotation about this bond.
  - There are two different groups on each carbon atom of the C=C group.
- A planar species of formula MX_2Y_2 or an octahedral species of formula MY_2Z_2, where Z is a bidentate group (see page 100).

The bond angle around the C=C carbon atoms is 120° and the molecules are planar.

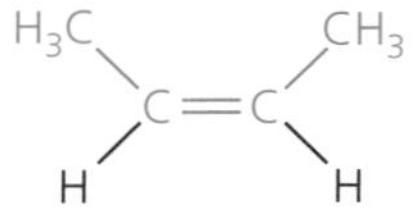

cis-but-2-ene

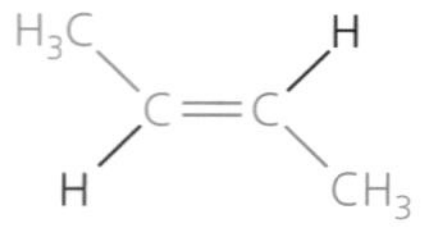

trans-but-2-ene

MUST REMEMBER

- **Geometric isomers** have almost **identical chemical properties** but **different physical properties** such as melting point.

Stereoisomers have the same structural formulae but the arrangement of the atoms in space is different.

OPTICAL ISOMERISM

- **Optical isomers** must have a chiral centre:
  - They do not have a centre of symmetry.
  - One isomer is a non-superimposable mirror image of the other, like a left and a right hand.
- Most common cause of optical isomerism is when there are four different groups bonded onto a central carbon atom.

The isomers must be drawn as mirror images of each other.

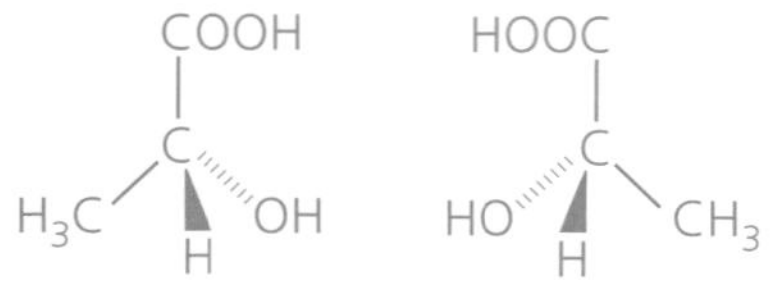

2-hydroxypropanoic acid (lactic acid) exists as two optical isomers.

MUST REMEMBER

- **Optical isomers** are chemically identical but their biochemical reactions are often different.
- They will **rotate the plane of polarisation of plane-polarised monochromatic light** in different directions.
- A **50/50 mixture** of optical isomers is called a **racemic mixture**. This mixture does not rotate the plane of polarised light.

WORKED EXAMPLE

One of the structural isomers of C_4H_9Cl exhibits stereoisomerism. Identify the type of isomerism and draw the two stereoisomers.

Optical isomerism

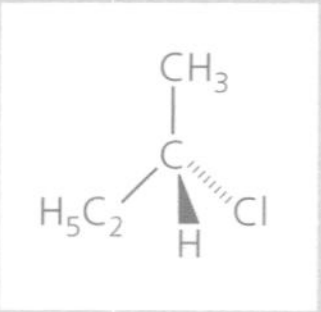

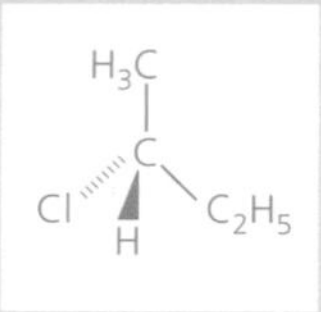

WORKED EXAMPLE

Draw and name the stereoisomers of 1,2-dichloroethene and identify the type of stereoisomerism.

Geometric isomerism

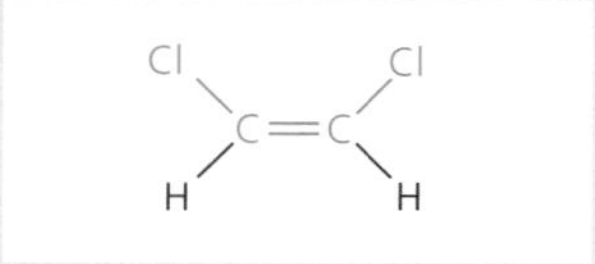

cis-1,2-dichloroethene

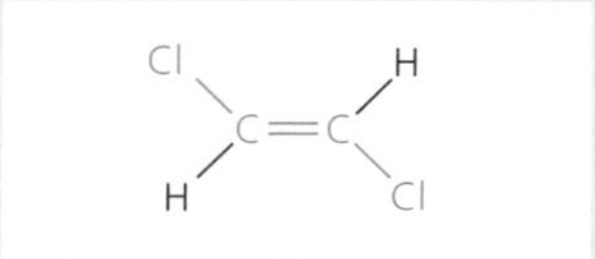

trans-1,2-dichloroethene

PROPERTIES OF CARBONYL COMPOUNDS

ALDEHYDES

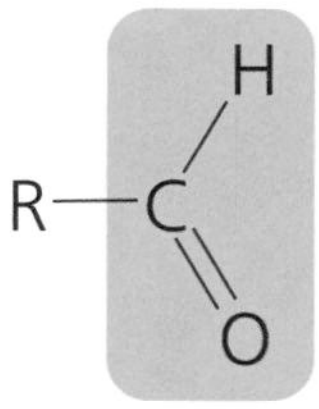

- R represents an alkyl group, e.g. CH_3 or CH_3CH_2, or an aryl group, e.g. C_6H_5.
- Methanal has two hydrogen atoms but no carbon atom joined to the carbonyl group.

KETONES

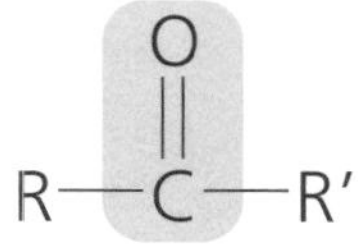

- R and R′ represent alkyl groups, e.g. CH_3 or CH_3CH_2, or aryl groups, e.g. C_6H_5.

FUNCTIONAL GROUP

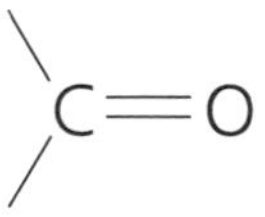

- The carbon and oxygen are **bonded** with a σ **bond** and a π **bond**.

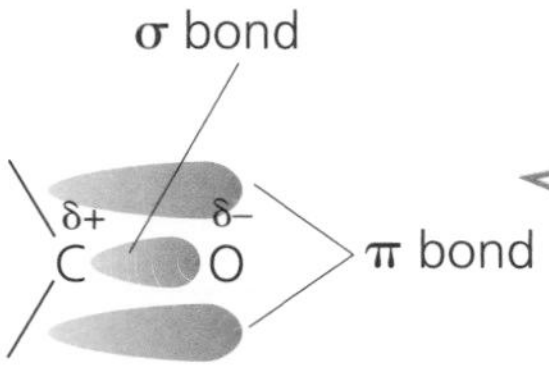

- Oxygen is more **electronegative** than carbon, and so the electrons in the double bond are drawn towards the **oxygen atom making it δ– and the carbon atom δ+.**

ALDEHYDES

Name	Formula
methanal	HCHO
ethanal	CH_3CHO
propanal	CH_3CH_2CHO
butanal	$CH_3CH_2CH_2CHO$
methylpropanal	$(CH_3)_2CHCHO$
benzaldehyde	C_6H_5CHO

KETONES

Name	Formula
propanone	CH_3COCH_3
butanone	$CH_3CH_2COCH_3$
pentan-2-one	$CH_3CH_2CH_2COCH_3$
pentan-3-one	$CH_3CH_2COCH_2CH_3$
phenylethanone	$C_6H_5COCH_3$

WORKED EXAMPLE

Write the structural formulae of
(a) 2-methylbutanone
(b) 2-phenylpropanal

(a)

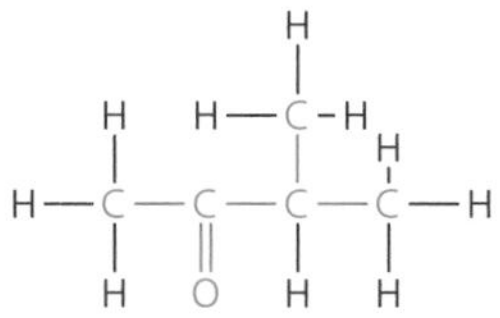

or

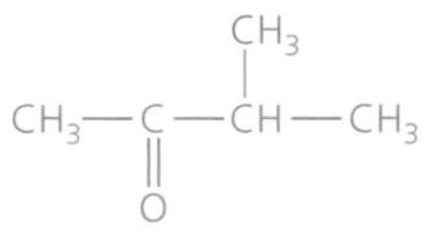

(b)

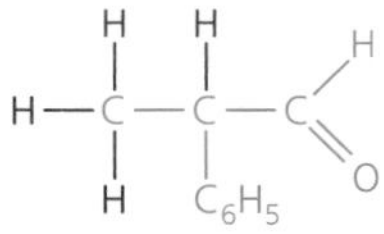

or

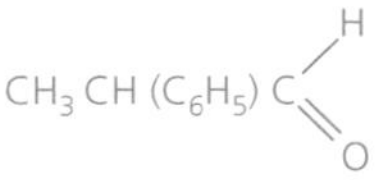

MUST TAKE CARE

Must never write the formula of an aldehyde as RCOH, as this implies an OH group as in alcohols and acids.

Must draw the C=O group showing the double bond if the structural formula is asked for.

WORKED EXAMPLE

Name the following
(a) $(CH_3)_2CHCOCH_3$
(b) $(CH_3)_3CCHO$

(a) 2-methylbutanone
(b) 2,2-dimethylpropanal

SOLUBILITY

- Carbonyl compounds with a small number of carbon atoms are soluble in water because they can form **hydrogen bonds** with water molecules.
- Large alkyl and aryl groups are **hydrophobic** which causes the solubility to decrease.
- Propanone is a good solvent for many organic substances, especially those containing an oxygen atom.

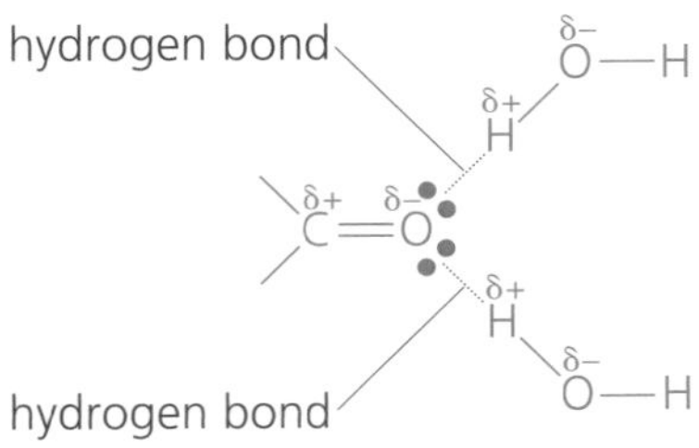

PHYSICAL PROPERTIES

SHAPE

- The carbon atom has three σ bonds and no lone pairs.
- These electron pairs repel to a position of maximum separation, which is **triangular planar** with a bond angle of 120°.

BOILING POINT

- Carbonyl compounds are polar but do not contain a δ+ hydrogen atom, so they cannot form intermolecular hydrogen bonds.
- Intermolecular forces involved are:
  - dipole–dipole forces
  - instantaneous induced dipole–induced dipole forces … also called **dispersion** or **van der Waals** forces.
- Their boiling points are lower than alcohols and carboxylic acids with similar molar masses because the latter can form strong hydrogen bonds as well as dipole–dipole and van der Waals forces between their molecules.
- Their boiling points are higher than alkanes or alkenes with similar molar masses, because the latter are non-polar and so do not form dipole–dipole forces between their molecules.
- Boiling point increases with the number of carbon atoms in each homologous series.
- Strength of dispersion / van der Waals forces depends mainly on number of electrons in the molecule and amount of contact between molecules.

WORKED EXAMPLE

Why is ethanal very soluble in water whereas pentan-1-ol is almost totally insoluble?

Ethanal can form hydrogen bonds between the δ+ hydrogen in the water and the δ– oxygen in the C=O group. Although pentan-1-ol can also hydrogen bond, it has a long non-polar chain which is hydrophobic and so causes insolubility.

WORKED EXAMPLE

State and explain the value of the CCC bond angle in propanone.

The carbonyl carbon atom forms three σ bonds (and one π bond) and has no lone pairs, so the electron groups repel each other to a position of maximum separation. This is triangular planar with a CCC bond angle of 120°.

WORKED EXAMPLE

Explain why the boiling points of propanal (49°C) and propanone (56°C) are similar but are much less than that of ethanoic acid, CH_3COOH (118°C).

Ethanoic acid can form intermolecular hydrogen bonds as it has a δ+ hydrogen and a δ– oxygen. Propanal and propanone cannot form intermolecular hydrogen bonds as neither has a δ+ hydrogen atom. Both form similar dipole–dipole forces as both have the same polar C=O group, and similar induced dipole–dipole forces as both have the same number of electrons in the molecule.

LABORATORY PREPARATION OF CARBONYL COMPOUNDS

ALDEHYDES

- Aldehydes are prepared by the controlled **oxidation** of a **primary alcohol**:
  - e.g. ethanal is prepared by oxidising ethanol with a solution of potassium dichromate(VI) in dilute sulphuric acid.
- Apparatus needed for preparation of ethanal is:

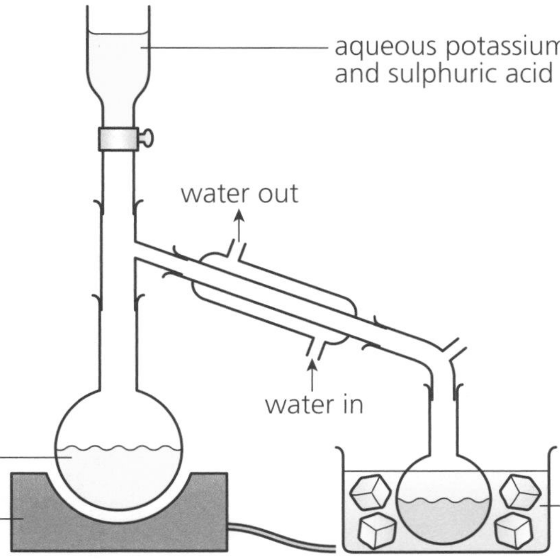

Distillation with addition

MUST TAKE CARE

Must make sure that the apparatus is **not sealed**, and that each part is drawn as a **separate piece** of equipment.

1. Ethanol is placed in the flask and heated, using an electric heater, to 60°C.
2. Mixture of potassium dichromate(VI) dissolved in dilute sulphuric acid is added from the tap funnel a small amount at a time.
3. Exothermic nature of the reaction maintains temperature at about 60°C and the ethanal is boiled off as it is formed.
4. The ethanal vapour condenses in the water-cooled condenser and collects in the receiving flask.

Reagents	Potassium dichromate(VI), sulphuric acid and ethanol (boiling point 79°C)
Products	Ethanal (boiling point 21°C), chromium(III) sulphate
Conditions	Maintain temperature between boiling points of ethanal and ethanol, **so ethanal boils off before it is further oxidised**
Observations	Orange solution turns green as $Cr_2O_7^{2-}$ ions are reduced to Cr^{3+} ions
Precautions	Do not use a Bunsen flame to heat the flask – ethanol and ethanal are both flammable Keep receiving flask immersed in iced water to prevent ethanal evaporating
Purification	Ethanal can be redistilled – collect the fraction that boils over between 20°C and 23°C
Equation	$CH_3CH_2OH + [O] \rightarrow CH_3CHO + H_2O$

[O] may be used to denote oxygen from an oxidising agent, but the equation must balance.

KETONES

- Ketones are prepared by heating a **secondary alcohol** under reflux with a suitable **oxidising agent**.
- Apparatus needed for preparation of propanone from propan-2-ol is:

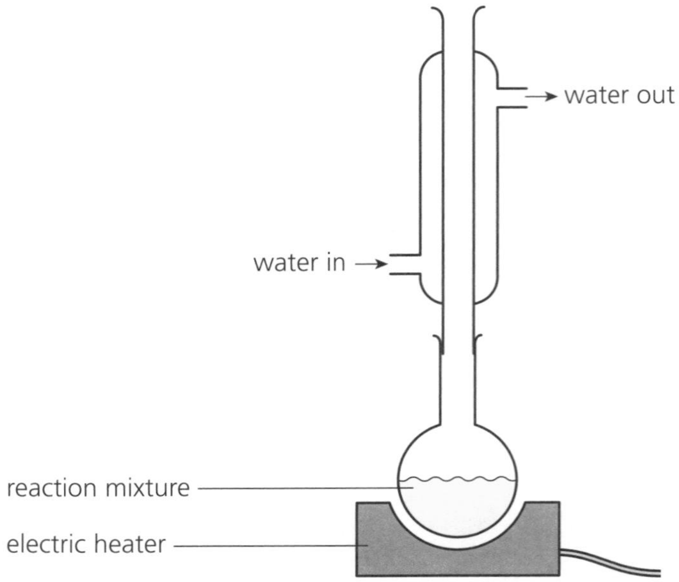

Heating under reflex

1. Place some propan-2-ol in a flask and add a solution of potassium dichromate(VI) in dilute sulphuric acid.
2. Fit a reflux condenser and heat mixture until it boils.
3. Continue to heat mixture for at least 15 minutes.
4. Allow to cool and change apparatus to distillation.
5. Distil off propanone between 54°C and 58°C.

MUST TAKE CARE

When drawing apparatus, must make sure that:

- Apparatus is not sealed.
- Top of the still-head in distillation has a **thermometer** or a **stopper**.
- Water flows **in at lower end of condenser and out at upper end**.
- Different parts of the apparatus are drawn as separate pieces and not in one long continuous piece of glassware.
- Apparatus works.

Reagents	Potassium dichromate(VI), sulphuric acid and propan-2-ol
Products	Propanone, chromium(III) sulphate
Conditions	Heat the mixture under reflux
Observations	Orange solution turns green as the $Cr_2O_7^{2-}$ ions are reduced to Cr^{3+} ions
Precautions	Do not use a Bunsen flame to heat the flask – propan-2-ol and propanone are both flammable
Equation	$CH_3CH(OH)CH_3 + [O] \rightarrow CH_3COCH_3 + H_2O$

[O] may be used to denote oxygen from an oxidising agent, but the equation must balance.

REACTIONS OF CARBONYL COMPOUNDS

REACTIONS OF BOTH ALDEHYDES AND KETONES

- C=O group is polar, with a δ+ carbon atom.
- This causes it to be attacked by **nucleophiles**.

MUST REMEMBER

- A **nucleophile** is a species with a **lone pair of electrons** which it uses to form a **covalent bond at a δ+ site.**

- C=C group in alkenes is not polar, but there is a uniform high electron density in the π bond above and below the σ bond which is on the line between the centres of the two carbon atoms.
- **This means that C=C group will be attacked by electrophiles** e.g.:
  - a bromine atom in Br_2
  - δ+ hydrogen in HBr.

NUCLEOPHILIC ADDITION

1. Addition of hydrogen cyanide, HCN

Reagent	Hydrogen cyanide
Conditions	The solution must be slightly alkaline, buffered at pH 8
Equation for reaction with ethanal	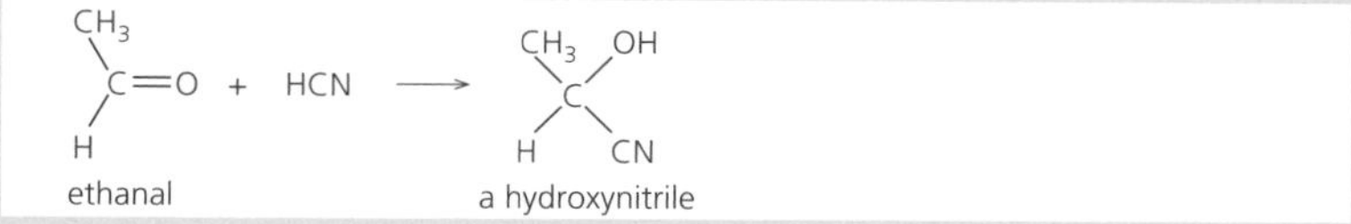
Product	2-hydroxypropanenitrile
Equation for reaction with propanone	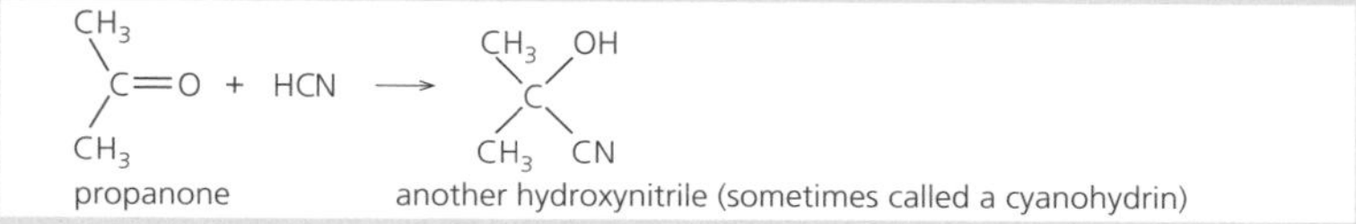
Product	2-hydroxy,2-methylpropanenitrile

The products are hydroxynitriles, which can be:

- reduced to amines by adding lithium tetrahydridoaluminate(III), $LiAlH_4$, in dry ether, **followed** by dilute acid.
  $CH_3CH(OH)CN + 4[H] \rightarrow CH_3CH(OH)CH_2NH_2$
- hydrolysed to hydroxyacids by heating under reflux with dilute sulphuric acid (or with sodium hydroxide and then acidifying with sulphuric acid to produce the acid from its sodium salt).
  $CH_3CH(OH)CN + H^+ + 2H_2O \rightarrow CH_3CH(OH)COOH + NH_4^+$
  2-hydroxypropanoic acid (lactic acid) is formed.

[H] may be used to denote hydrogen from a reducing agent, but the equation must balance.

Mechanism

Hydrogen cyanide is too weak a nucleophile to cause a reaction.

Step 1: the alkali deprotonates some of the HCN forming **⁻CN ions**. The lone pair on the negative carbon atom forms a bond with the δ+ **carbonyl carbon atom**.

Step 2: the negative oxygen in the intermediate removes a proton (H^+) from an HCN molecule, forming a CN^- ion. This continues the reaction.

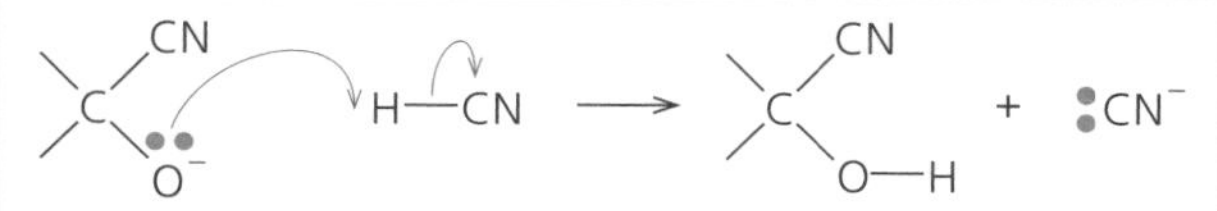

2. Addition of hydrogen

- C=O group is reduced to a CH(OH) group.

Reagent	Sodium tetrahydridoborate(III), $NaBH_4$
Conditions	Mix in an aqueous solution
Equation for reaction with ethanal	$CH_3CHO + 2[H] \rightarrow CH_3CH_2OH$
Product	Ethanol
Equation for reaction with propanone	$CH_3COCH_3 + 2[H] \rightarrow CH_3CH(OH)CH_3$
Product	Propan-2-ol

This reaction is also carried out by **lithium tetrahydridoaluminate(III)**, $LiAlH_4$, in **dry ether, followed by dilute acid.**

Mechanism

Step 1: **attack by H^- ion** in the sodium tetrahydridoborate(III) – this adds to the δ+ carbon atom.

Step 2: negatively-charged oxygen atom removes a H^+ ion from a water molecule.

CONDENSATION REACTION

- This is addition followed by elimination.
- Takes place with substances containing the $H_2N–NH$ group.

Reagent	2,4-dinitrophenylhydrazine – a solution of this is called Brady's reagent
Conditions	Add a few drops of the carbonyl compound to a solution of 2,4-dinitrophenylhydrazine
Observation	Yellow or orange precipitate is formed – **this reaction is a test for carbonyl compounds**
Equation for ethanal	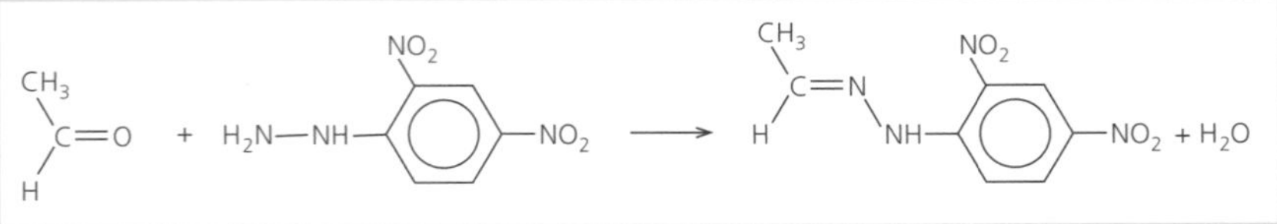
Product	Ethanal 2,4-dintrophenylhydrazone

Mechanism

Step 1: lone pair of electrons on the nitrogen forms a bond with the δ+ carbon atom.

Step 2: water is then lost from this intermediate.

REACTIONS OF ALDEHYDES ONLY

OXIDATION

Aldehydes can be oxidised to carboxylic acids.

$$RCHO + [O] \rightarrow RCOOH$$

Reagent	Potassium dichromate(VI) (or potassium manganate(VII)) in dilute sulphuric acid
Observation	Orange $Cr_2O_7^{2-}$ ions are reduced to a green solution of Cr^{3+} ions when mixed with aldehydes

Ketones do not react so the solution would stay orange.

Reagent	**Fehling's** solution which is a copper(II) complex
Conditions	Warm the aldehyde with Fehling's solution
Observation	Blue copper(II) tartrate complex is reduced to a **red precipitate** of copper(I) oxide
Product	Aldehyde is oxidised to the **carboxylate anion** because the solution is alkaline

Benedict's solution is another blue copper(II) complex and reacts in the same way with aldehydes.

Ketones do not react so the solution would stay blue.

Reagent	**A complex of Ag^+ ions** with ammonia, $[Ag(NH_3)_2]^+(aq)$
Conditions	Warm the aldehyde with a solution made by adding excess ammonia solution to aqueous silver nitrate
Observation	Silver(I) complex is reduced to a **silver mirror**
Product	Aldehyde is oxidised to the carboxylate anion because the solution is alkaline

Tollens' reagent is another silver(I) complex and is also reduced to a silver mirror by aldehydes.

Ketones do not reduce this complex.

MUST REMEMBER

- The reactions of **Fehling's or Benedict's solution** and of **ammoniacal silver nitrate** may be used as a **test for aldehydes**.

THE IODOFORM (TRIIODOMETHANE) REACTION

All ketones containing the CH_3CO group and ethanal will undergo this reaction.

Reagent	Solution of iodine in sodium hydroxide
Conditions	Warm gently
Observation	Pale yellow precipitate (of CHI_3) forms
Equation with propanone	$CH_3COCH_3 + 3I_2 + 4NaOH \rightarrow CHI_3 + CH_3COONa + 3NaI + 3H_2O$

- This reaction is also performed by secondary methyl alcohols, which contain the $CH_3CH(OH)$ group, and by ethanol.
- These alcohols are oxidised by the iodine in alkali to methyl ketones, which contain the CH_3CO group, or to ethanal.

TESTS

FOR CARBONYL COMPOUNDS

Test	Add it to a solution of **2,4-dinitrophenylhydrazine**
Observation	Carbonyl compounds give a yellow or orange precipitate
Test	Observe the infra-red spectrum
Observation	Aldehydes and ketones, like all other compounds with a C=O group such as acids, esters etc, have a strong absorption at a wavenumber ~1700 cm^{-1}

TO DISTINGUISH BETWEEN ALDEHYDES AND KETONES

Test	Warm with **Fehling's** (or Benedict's) solution
Observation	**Aldehydes** produce a **red** precipitate **Ketones** leave blue colour **unchanged**
Test	Warm with a solution of silver nitrate in aqueous ammonia (or with **Tollens'** reagent)
Observation	**Aldehydes** produce a **silver mirror** on the wall of the test tube **Ketones have no reaction**

KEY POINTS

REACTIONS OF ALDEHYDES

RCHO

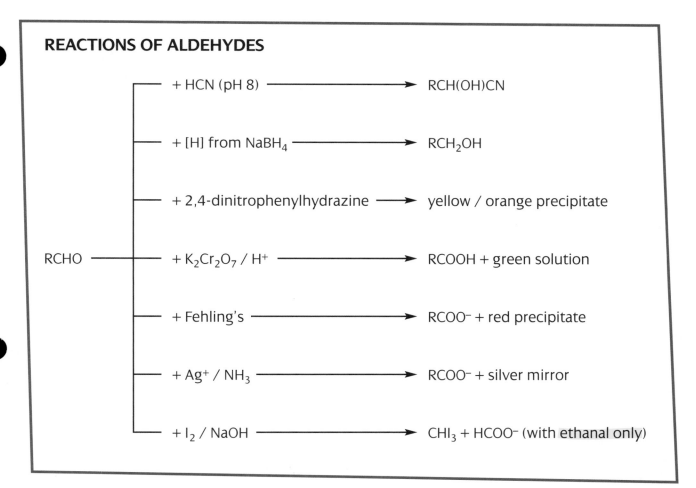

+ HCN (pH 8) →	RCH(OH)CN
+ [H] from $NaBH_4$ →	RCH_2OH
+ 2,4-dinitrophenylhydrazine →	yellow / orange precipitate
+ $K_2Cr_2O_7$ / H^+ →	RCOOH + green solution
+ Fehling's →	$RCOO^-$ + red precipitate
+ Ag^+ / NH_3 →	$RCOO^-$ + silver mirror
+ I_2 / NaOH →	CHI_3 + $HCOO^-$ (with ethanal only)

REACTIONS OF KETONES

RCOR′

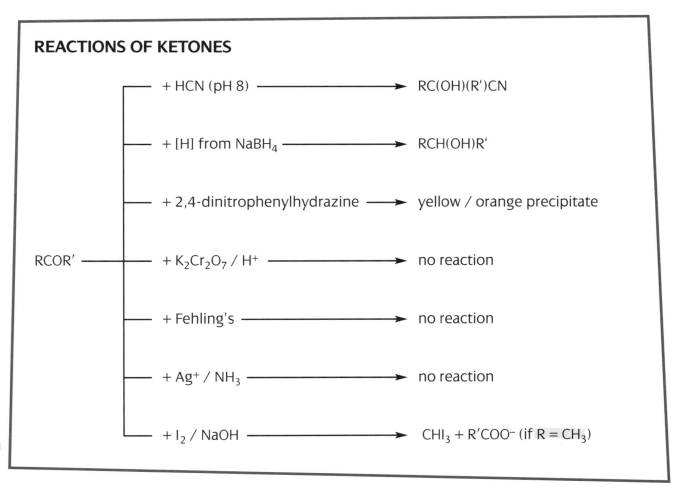

+ HCN (pH 8) →	RC(OH)(R')CN
+ [H] from $NaBH_4$ →	RCH(OH)R'
+ 2,4-dinitrophenylhydrazine →	yellow / orange precipitate
+ $K_2Cr_2O_7$ / H^+ →	no reaction
+ Fehling's →	no reaction
+ Ag^+ / NH_3 →	no reaction
+ I_2 / NaOH →	CHI_3 + $R'COO^-$ (if $R = CH_3$)

WORKED EXAMPLE

Write the formula of the product of reacting the compound causing the smell of lemons

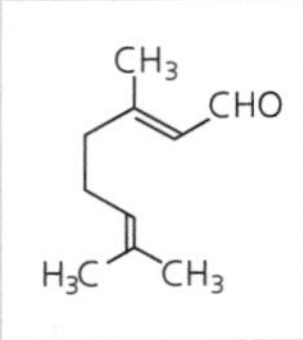

with

(a) sodium tetrahydridoborate(III), $NaBH_4$
(b) hydrogen and a platinum catalyst

(a)

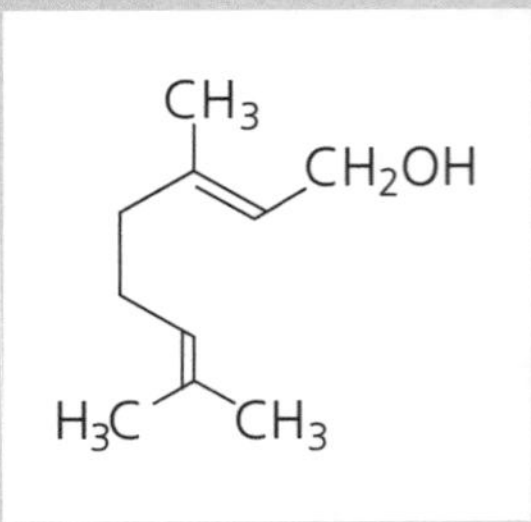

(b)

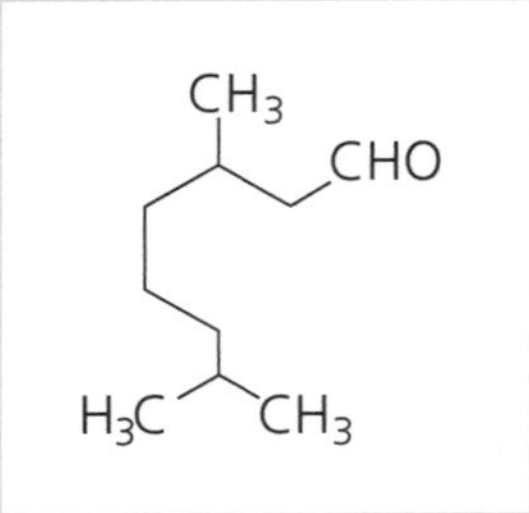

Sodium tetrahydridoborate(III) only reduces polar double bonds, such as in the C=O group, and does not attack the electron rich C=C group.

Hydrogen adds on to both the C=C groups and not to the polar C=O group.

WORKED EXAMPLE

Write the formulae of the organic products, if any, of reacting butanone with

(a) hydrogen cyanide
(b) Fehling's solution
(c) 2,4-dintrophenylhydrazine
(d) iodine in aqueous sodium hydroxide

(a) $CH_3CH_2C(OH)(CN)CH_3$
(b) No reaction
(c)

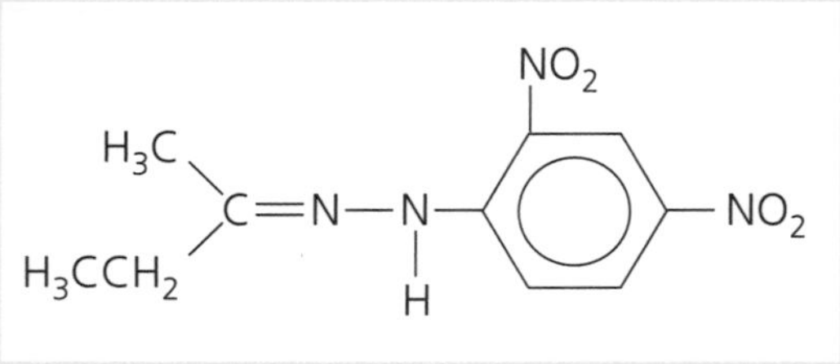

(d) CHI_3 and $CH_3CH_2COO^-Na^+$

GRIGNARD REAGENTS

start
Edexcel only

- **Grignard reagents** consist of an alkyl group, such as C_2H_5, bonded to a magnesium atom which is also bonded to a halogen.
- The carbon–magnesium covalent bond is highly polar with the carbon atom δ– and the magnesium δ+.

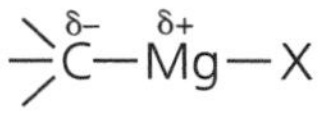

- The δ– carbon atom acts as a **nucleophile** and attacks δ+ carbon atoms forming a new carbon–carbon σ bond.
- The δ– carbon atom in the Grignard reagent attacks the δ+ carbon atom in the C=O group. The intermediate formed has then to be hydrolysed by adding an aqueous acid, such as dilute HCl.

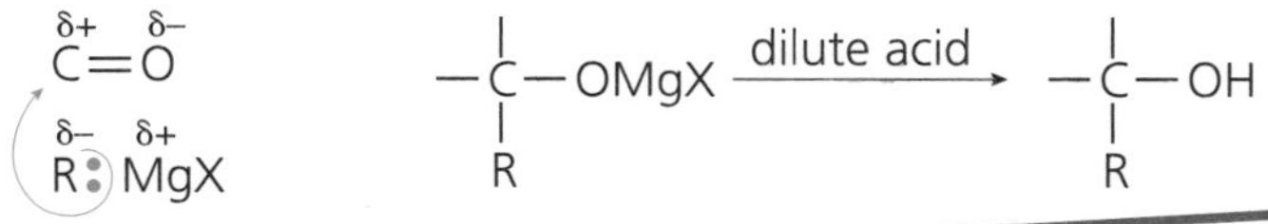

PREPARATION

- Grignard reagents are prepared by refluxing a halogenoalkane with magnesium in a solution of dry ether (ethoxyethane).
- A crystal of iodine may be needed as a catalyst.
  $C_2H_5Br + Mg \rightarrow C_2H_5MgBr$
- Reagents: bromoethane and magnesium
- Conditions: reflux in dry ether solvent
- Product: ethylmagnesium bromide

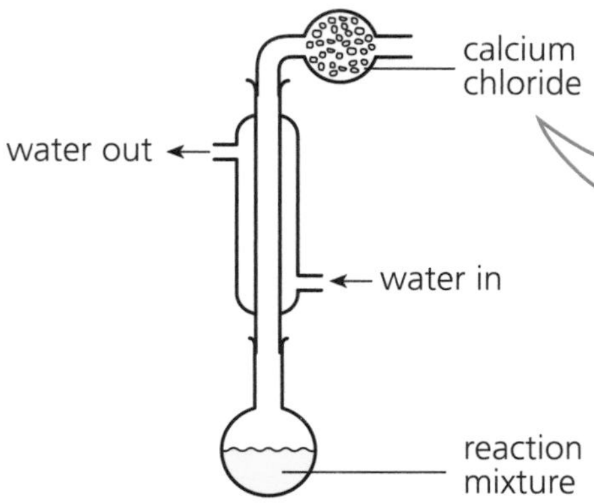

Apparatus for preparation of Grignard reagents

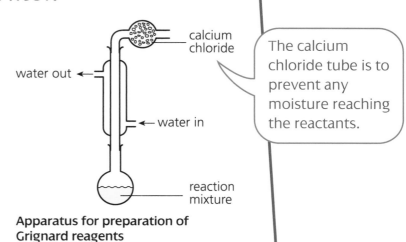

The calcium chloride tube is to prevent any moisture reaching the reactants.

REACTIONS OF GRIGNARD REAGENTS

+ WATER

- Grignard reagents are rapidly hydrolysed to alkanes by water:
  $C_2H_5MgBr + H_2O \rightarrow C_2H_6 + Mg(OH)Br$
- It is because of this reaction that the chemicals and apparatus must be dry when preparing a Grignard reagent.

+ CARBON DIOXIDE

- The δ– carbon atom in the Grignard reagent attacks the δ+ carbon in CO_2. The intermediate is hydrolysed and a carboxylic acid is formed with one more carbon atom than there was in the Grignard.
- Ethylmagnesium bromide forms propanoic acid:
  $CH_3CH_2MgBr + CO_2 \longrightarrow CH_3CH_2COOH$
- Conditions: add dry ice (solid CO_2) or pass carbon dioxide gas into the solution of the Grignard reagent in dry ether. Then hydrolyse the intermediate with dilute HCl.

+ CARBONYL COMPOUNDS

- Grignard reagents react with aldehydes and ketones to form alcohols.

Formation of a primary alcohol

- A Grignard reagent and methanal form a 1° alcohol:

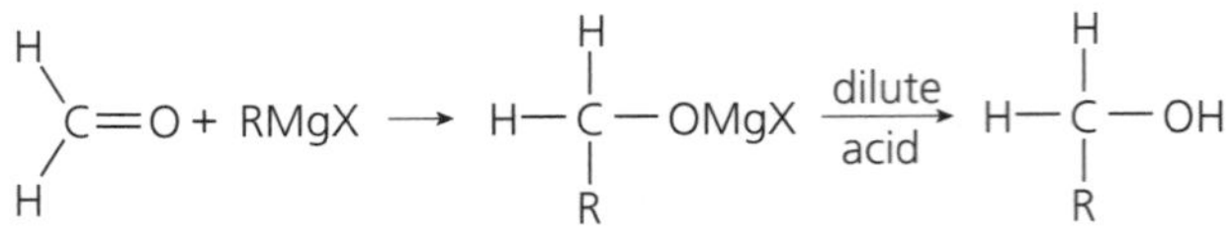

- 1-propylmagnesium bromide and methanal form butan-1-ol after the intermediate has been hydrolysed by acid:
$CH_3CH_2CH_2MgBr + HCHO \rightarrow CH_3CH_2CH_2CH_2OH$

Formation of a secondary alcohol

- All other aldehydes form 2° alcohols:

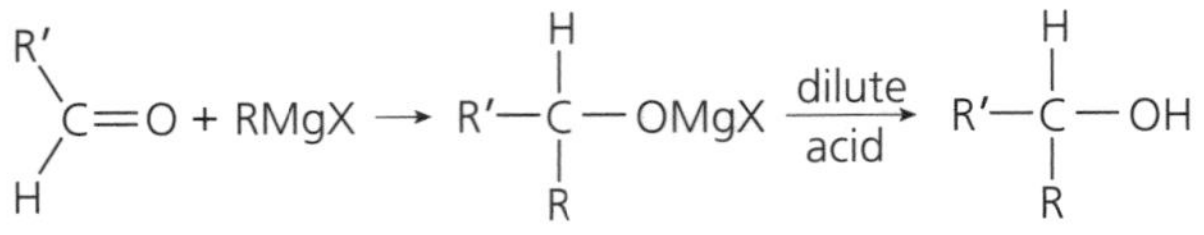

- Butan-2-ol is formed from ethylmagnesium bromide and ethanal, after hydrolysis of the intermediate:
$CH_3CH_2MgBr + CH_3CHO \rightarrow CH_3CH_2CH(OH)CH_3$

Formation of a tertiary alcohol

- Ketones react with Grignard reagents to form 3° alcohols:

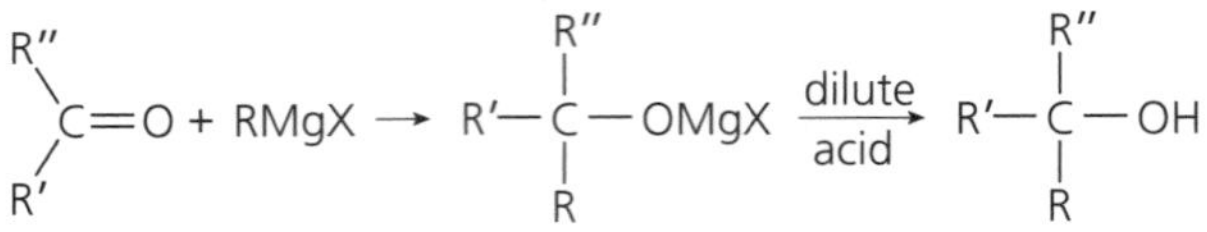

- Ethylmagnesium bromide and propanone form 2-methyl,butan-2-ol:
$CH_3CH_2MgBr + CH_3COCH_3 \rightarrow (CH_3)_2C(OH)CH_2CH_3$

ORGANIC SYNTHESES

- Grignard reagents are one of the few ways of increasing the carbon chain length.

INCREASE BY 1

- Add the Grignard reagent to methanal to get a 1° alcohol
- Add CO_2 to the Grignard reagent to get a carboxylic acid
- Add methylmagnesium bromide to a carbonyl compound or to carbon dioxide

INCREASE BY 2

- Add the Grignard reagent to ethanal to get a 2° alcohol
- Add ethylmagnesium bromide to a carbonyl compound

INCREASE BY 3

- Add the Grignard reagent to propanal to get a 2° alcohol or to propanone to get a 3° alcohol
- Add propylmagnesium bromide to a carbonyl compound

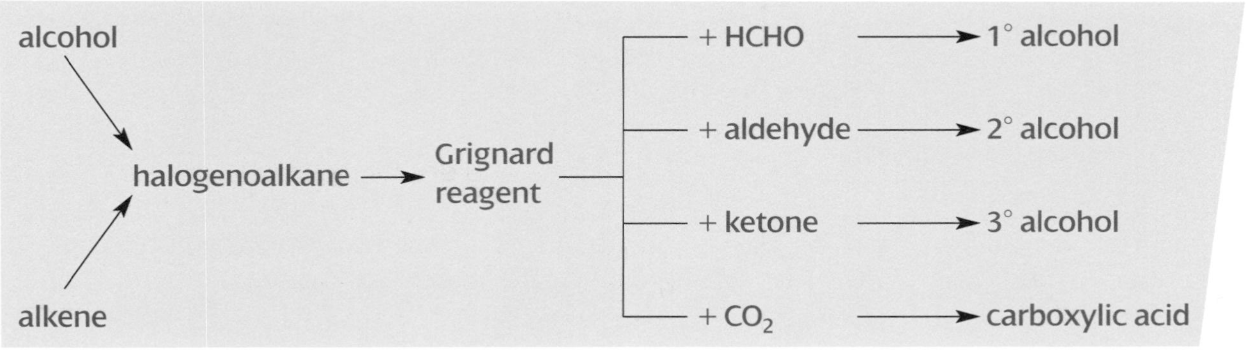

end
Edexcel only

CARBOXYLIC ACIDS

TESTS FOR THE COOH GROUP

Test	Observation
Add PCl_5	Carboxylic acids give steamy fumes of HCl because they contain the OH group
Test with damp blue litmus	Litmus turns red
Add it to a solution of sodium hydrogencarbonate	Fizzing – gas evolved turns limewater cloudy

MUST TAKE CARE

Alcohols and water also give steamy fumes with PCl_5.

SOLUBILITY

- Carboxylic acids with a low molar mass dissolve in water.
- This is because they have a δ– oxygen and a δ+ hydrogen . . . so can form hydrogen bonds with the water.

FUNCTIONAL GROUP

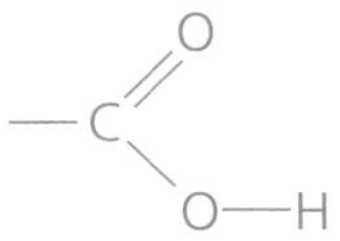

Stem name (ethan-, propan- etc) is given by total number of carbon atoms in the chain, **including the carbon of the COOH group**.

Name	Formula
methanoic acid	HCOOH
ethanoic acid	CH_3COOH
propanoic acid	CH_3CH_2COOH
butanoic acid	$CH_3CH_2CH_2COOH$
methylpropanoic acid	$(CH_3)_2CHCOOH$

- **Molecular formula must be unambiguous**: C_3H_7COOH could be butanoic acid or methylpropanoic acid.
- **Structural formula must show bonding in the functional group.** Structural formula of propanoic acid is:

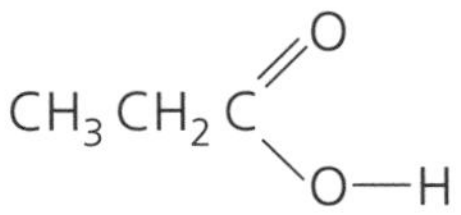

- **Full structural formula** or a displayed formula **must show all the atoms and their bonds**. Full structural formula of propanoic acid is:

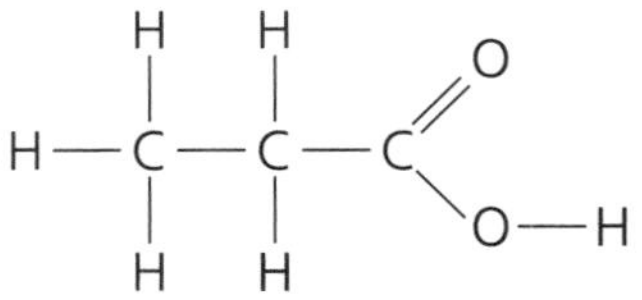

For practice in answering A2 Chemistry questions, why not use *Collins Do Brilliantly A2 Chemistry*?

PREPARATION OF CARBOXYLIC ACIDS

OXIDATION OF PRIMARY ALCOHOLS

- Propan-1-ol is oxidised by heating under reflux with excess of a solution of potassium dichromate(VI) in sulphuric acid. Propanoic acid is the product:

  $CH_3CH_2CH_2OH + 2[O] \rightarrow CH_3CH_2COOH + H_2O$

THE IODOFORM REACTION

- When a methyl ketone (one containing the CH_3CO group) is warmed with iodine and aqueous sodium hydroxide, iodoform, CHI_3, and the salt of a carboxylic acid is formed. Butanone gives sodium propanoate:

  $$CH_3CH_2COCH_3 \xrightarrow{OH^- + I_2} CHI_3 + CH_3CH_2COO^-$$

- On addition of a strong acid, propanoic acid is formed.

  $CH_3CH_2COO^- + H^+ \rightarrow CH_3CH_2COOH$

HYDROLYSIS OF NITRILES

- Propanenitrile, CH_3CH_2CN, is hydrolysed by boiling under reflux with dilute sulphuric acid. The product is propanoic acid:

  $CH_3CH_2CN + 2H_2O + H^+ \rightarrow CH_3CH_2COOH + NH_4^+$

- Propanenitrile can be made from chloroethane and potassium cyanide.

CH_3CH_2COOH

- 2-hydroxypropanenitrile, $CH_3CH(OH)CN$, is hydrolysed to 2-hydroxypropanoic acid (lactic acid):

  $CH_3CH(OH)CN + 2H_2O + H^+$
  $\rightarrow CH_3CH(OH)COOH + NH_4^+$

- $CH_3CH(OH)CN$ can be made by the nucleophilic addition reaction of HCN with propanone.

REACTIONS OF CARBOXYLIC ACIDS

ESTERIFICATION

REDUCTION

$+ PCl_5$

AS AN ACID

ESTERIFICATION

- When a carboxylic acid is warmed under reflux with an alcohol and a trace of conc. sulphuric acid, an **ester** is formed in a reversible reaction:
  carboxylic acid + alcohol ⇌ ester + water

  $CH_3COOH + C_2H_5OH \rightleftharpoons CH_3COOC_2H_5 + H_2O$

  ethanoic acid + ethanol ⇌ ethylethanoate + water

AS AN ACID

- Carboxylic acids are weak acids.
- Their aqueous solutions have a pH of about 3.
- They react with bases, such as sodium hydroxide, to form a salt:
  $CH_3COOH + NaOH \rightarrow CH_3COONa + H_2O$
- They react with carbonates and hydrogencarbonates to give carbon dioxide gas:
  $2CH_3COOH + Na_2CO_3 \rightarrow 2CH_3COONa + CO_2 + H_2O$
  $CH_3COOH + NaHCO_3 \rightarrow CH_3COONa + CO_2 + H_2O$

REDUCTION

- Carboxylic acids can be **reduced** to a primary alcohol using lithium tetrahydridoaluminate(III) in dry ether solution:
  $CH_3COOH + 4[H] \rightarrow CH_3CH_2OH + H_2O$
- 2-stage reaction – first the acid is warmed with the reducing agent, and then dilute acid is added to free the alcohol.

$+ PCl_5$

- **Phosphorus pentachloride** reacts vigorously with acids to form an acid chloride:
  $CH_3COOH + PCl_5 \rightarrow CH_3COCl + POCl_3 + HCl$
- Steamy fumes of hydrogen chloride are produced which form a white smoke with gaseous ammonia.

ACID CHLORIDES AND ACID ANHYDRIDES

start not OCR

ACID CHLORIDES

Acid chlorides contain the 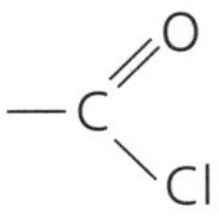 group.

- Prepared from a carboxylic acid and PCl_5.
- React with nucleophiles.
- React faster than acids because the C–Cl bond is weaker than the C–OH bond.

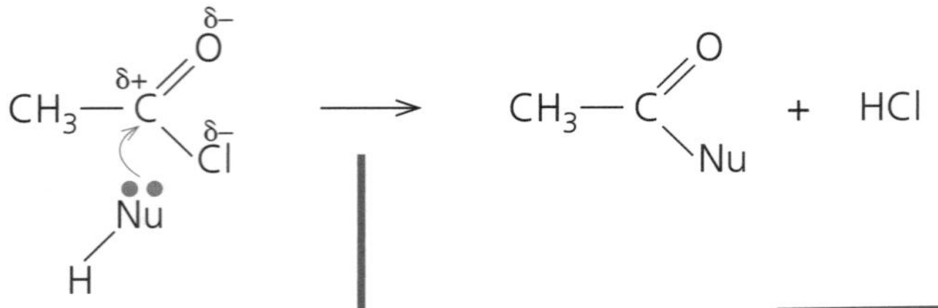

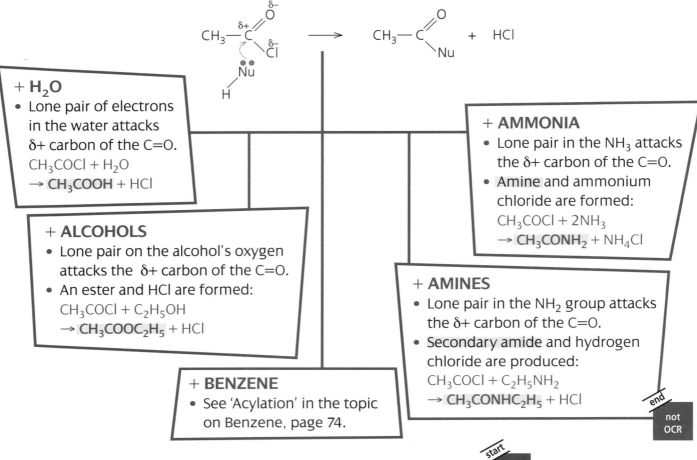

+ H_2O
- Lone pair of electrons in the water attacks δ+ carbon of the C=O.

$CH_3COCl + H_2O$
→ **CH_3COOH** + HCl

+ ALCOHOLS
- Lone pair on the alcohol's oxygen attacks the δ+ carbon of the C=O.
- An ester and HCl are formed:

$CH_3COCl + C_2H_5OH$
→ **$CH_3COOC_2H_5$** + HCl

+ BENZENE
- See 'Acylation' in the topic on Benzene, page 74.

+ AMMONIA
- Lone pair in the NH_3 attacks the δ+ carbon of the C=O.
- Amine and ammonium chloride are formed:

$CH_3COCl + 2NH_3$
→ **CH_3CONH_2** + NH_4Cl

+ AMINES
- Lone pair in the NH_2 group attacks the δ+ carbon of the C=O.
- Secondary amide and hydrogen chloride are produced:

$CH_3COCl + C_2H_5NH_2$
→ **$CH_3CONHC_2H_5$** + HCl

end not OCR

start AQA only

ACID ANHYDRIDES

Acid anhydrides contain two acyl groups linked by an oxygen atom.

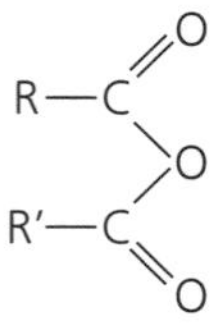

- Ethanoic anhydride reacts with the same reagents (other than with benzene) as ethanoyl chloride.
- The main product is the same, but instead of HCl or NH_4Cl being produced, ethanoic acid or ammonium ethanoate is formed.

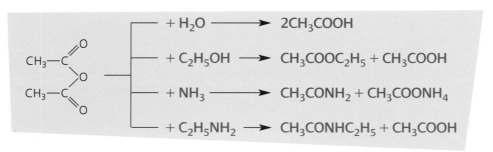

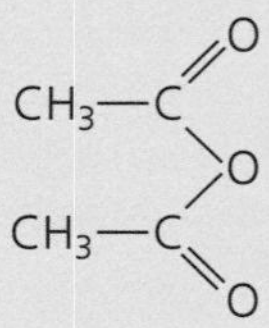

+ H_2O ⟶ $2CH_3COOH$

+ C_2H_5OH ⟶ $CH_3COOC_2H_5 + CH_3COOH$

+ NH_3 ⟶ $CH_3CONH_2 + CH_3COONH_4$

+ $C_2H_5NH_2$ ⟶ $CH_3CONHC_2H_5 + CH_3COOH$

end AQA only

ESTERS

Esters contain the 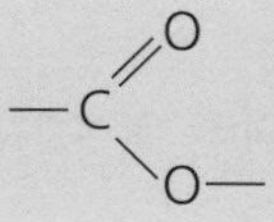 group.

PREPARATION

- **Esters** can be made by reacting an alcohol with one of three substances.

1.	Carboxylic acids	Mix acid and alcohol with a few drops of conc. H_2SO_4 and warm under reflux. $CH_3COOH + C_2H_5OH \rightleftharpoons CH_3COOC_2H_5 + H_2O$
2.	Acid chlorides (not required by OCR)	On mixing, a rapid exothermic reaction takes place with a good yield of ester. $CH_3COCl + C_2H_5OH \rightarrow CH_3COOC_2H_5 + HCl$
3.	Acid anhydrides (only required by AQA)	On warming a controlled and high-yield reaction takes place. $(CH_3CO)_2O + C_2H_5OH \rightarrow CH_3COOC_2H_5 + CH_3COOH$

- Aspirin is an ester of salicylic acid, HOC_6H_4COOH, and ethanoic acid. Its preparation is best done by reacting salicylic acid with ethanoic anhydride.
- This is a controlled high-yield reaction.
- The reaction with ethanoyl chloride is liable to give unwanted side reactions.

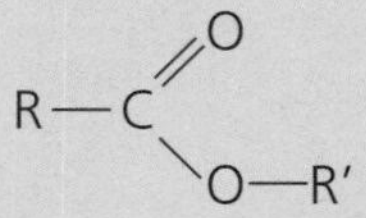

HYDROLYSIS

- Esters are **hydrolysed** by boiling under reflux with a solution of either an acid or an alkali:

$$CH_3COOC_2H_5 + H_2O \overset{H^+ \text{ catalyst}}{\rightleftharpoons} CH_3COOH + C_2H_5OH$$

$$CH_3COOC_2H_5 + NaOH \rightarrow CH_3COONa + C_2H_5OH$$

- The second reaction is more useful as it is irreversible and so the yield is high.

USES OF ESTERS

- Ingredients in some perfumes
- Food flavourings
- Good solvents for non-polar substances
- Can be mixed with some plastics to make them more flexible

- Soap is made by hydrolysing natural esters such as propan-1,2,3-tristearate. This ester is present in animal fat. If the fat is boiled with concentrated sodium hydroxide solution, propan-1,2,3-triol and sodium stearate are formed. Sodium stearate is a natural soap.

$CH_2OOCC_{17}H_{35}$
|
$CHOOCC_{17}H_{35} + 3NaOH \rightarrow CH_2(OH)CH(OH)CH_2OH + 3C_{17}H_{35}COONa$
|
$CH_2OOCC_{17}H_{35}$

- Vegetable oils, such as olive oil or palm oil, can also be hydrolysed in this way. They also produce soap.

POLYESTERS

Polyesters (and polyamides) are examples of **condensation polymers**.

- Made from two different monomers, each having two functional groups – one at each end.
- An analogy is short pieces of wire, some with a hook at each end and others with an eye at each end.

DEFINITION

When the two different monomers form a condensation polymer, they join together and eliminate a small molecule such as water at each join.

SIZE AND STRENGTH

- The polymer consists of thousands of monomers joined together, with an average relative molecular mass of around 10 000.
- When the fibres are stretched, the individual chains become parallel to each other… causing more van der Waals forces between the chains which strengthen the fibre.

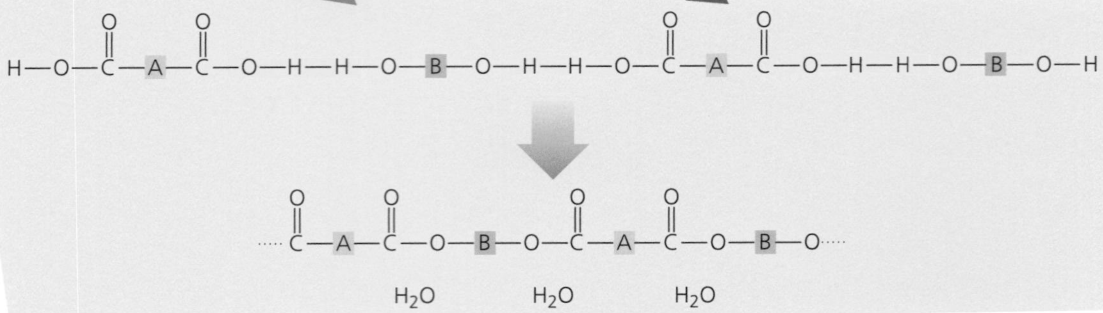

TERYLENE

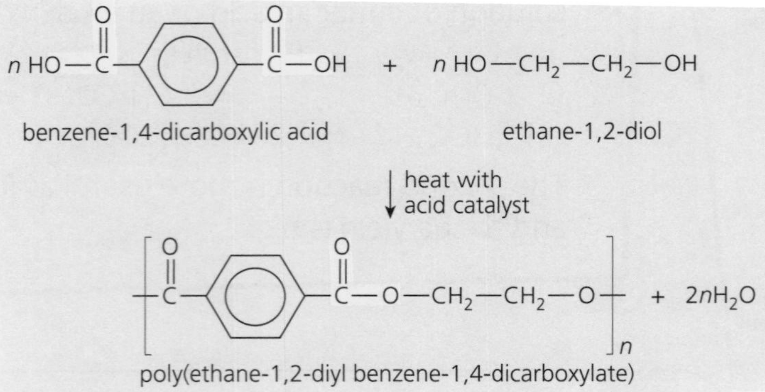

USES

Uses	Properties
Clothing (especially when mixed with cotton)	Crease-resistant Rot-proof as it is nonbiodegradable
Duvets	Good thermal insulator
Fizzy drink bottles	Shatterproof

THE ESTER LINK

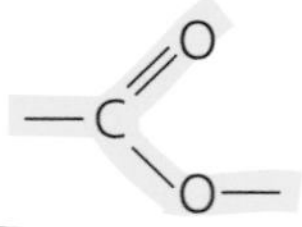

DISPOSAL

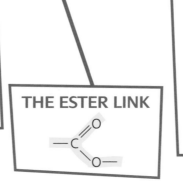

- Enzymes have not evolved to hydrolyse the ester link in terylene so it is not broken down biologically and will remain in landfill sites.
- Combustion at too low a temperature can cause toxic fumes.

AMIDES

start Edexcel only

PREPARATION

- **Amides** can be made from an acid chloride (or anhydride) and ammonia:

$CH_3COCl + NH_3 \rightarrow CH_3CONH_2 + HCl$

ethanoyl chloride — ethanamide

MELTING POINT AND SOLUBILITY

- Amides contain δ+ hydrogen atoms (on the NH_2 group), a δ– oxygen and a δ– nitrogen so they form hydrogen bonds with other molecules . . . causing them to be solid at room temperature.
- Amides form hydrogen bonds with δ+ hydrogen atoms and δ– oxygen atoms in water molecules so they dissolve in water.

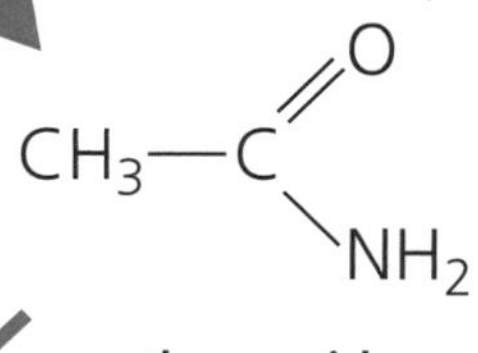

ethanamide

DEHYDRATION

- Amides can be dehydrated by phosphorus(V) oxide to a nitrile:

$$CH_3CONH_2 \xrightarrow{P_2O_5} CH_3CN$$

ethanamide — ethanenitrile

HOFMANN DEGRADATION

- When treated with liquid bromine and concentrated sodium hydroxide, an amide will form an amine with one fewer carbon atom:

$$CH_3CONH_2 \xrightarrow{Br_2(l)\ /\ NaOH(aq)} CH_3NH_2$$

ethanamide — methylamine

HYDROLYSIS

- Amides are hydrolysed on boiling under reflux with acids or alkalis:

$CH_3CONH_2 + H^+ + H_2O \rightarrow CH_3COOH + NH_4^+$

$CH_3CONH_2 + OH^- \rightarrow CH_3COO^- + NH_3$

end Edexcel only

POLYAMIDES

AMINO ACIDS

DIACID CHLORIDE AND DIAMINE

enzymes

POLYAMIDES

NYLON

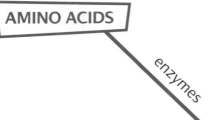

- Made by **polymerising** a diacid, such as 1,6-hexanedioic acid, with a diamine, such as 1,6-diaminohexane.

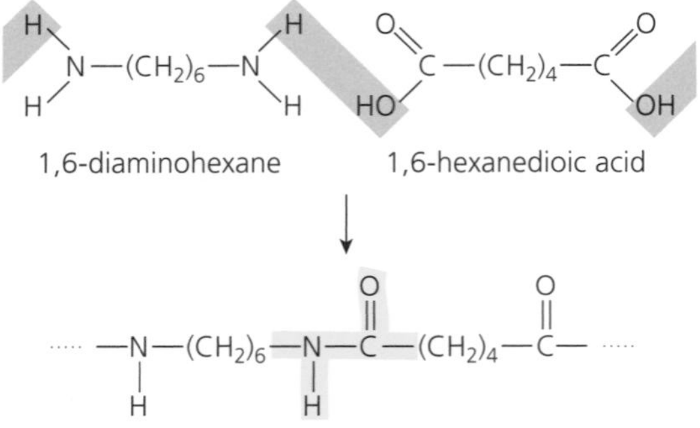

part of a nylon polymer chain

- In the laboratory the diacid chloride $ClOC(CH_2)_4COCl$ is used in place of the diacid.
- Kevlar is made from

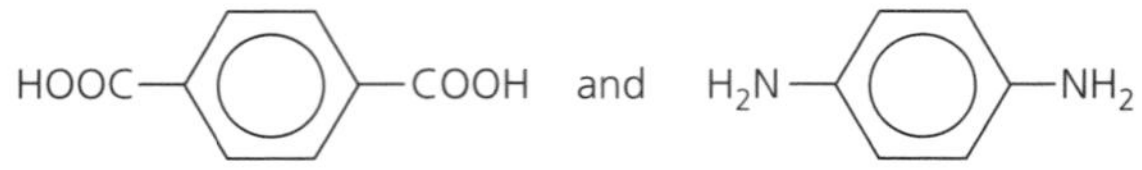

PROTEINS

- **Proteins** consist of a long chain of amino acids joined with peptide bonds.
- The chains in their structure are arranged in a helix or a pleated sheet, held together by hydrogen bonds between the δ+ hydrogen of the NH group and the δ– oxygen of the C=O group.
- Amino acids all have the general formula $RCH(NH_2)COOH$, where R can be a variety of different groups.

THE PEPTIDE LINK

- All proteins and polyamides contain the **peptide link** – the join between the amino acids or the monomers.

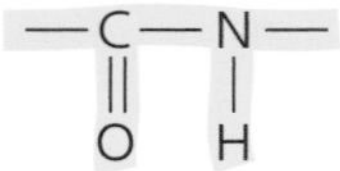

ADDITION POLYMERS

- **Addition polymers** are formed when monomers join together and no small molecules are eliminated.
- The monomer must have a double bond.
- The simplest is the result of polymerising ethene, $CH_2{=}CH_2$, to form poly(ethene).

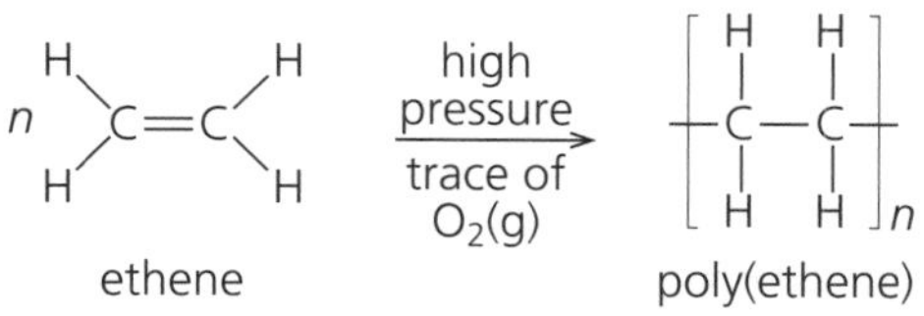

INITIATION STEP

- A substance which produces free radicals is added.

R–O–O–R ⟶ 2R—O•

FREE RADICAL POLYMERISATION

- A free radical is a species in which an atom has an unpaired electron – this is shown as a dot.

PROPAGATION STEPS

- One of these radicals breaks the π bond in an ethene molecule and forms a new radical. This breaks the π bond in another ethene molecule and on and on until thousands of ethene molecules have formed a long chain.

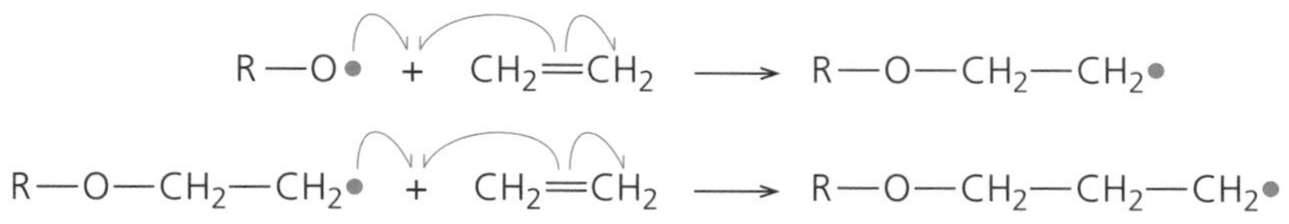

IONIC POLYMERISATION

- Catalysts such as $TiCl_4$ and $Al(C_2H_5)_3$ can be used in the polymerisation resulting in long linear chains.
- Van der Waals forces are stronger in this type of polymer because the chains lie parallel to each other.
- As there are more points of contact for the intermolecular forces, the result is a higher density, higher melting point polymer.

CHAIN BRANCHING

- Some radicals bend back and remove a hydrogen from the middle of the chain and form a radical with the unpaired electron now in the middle of the chain.

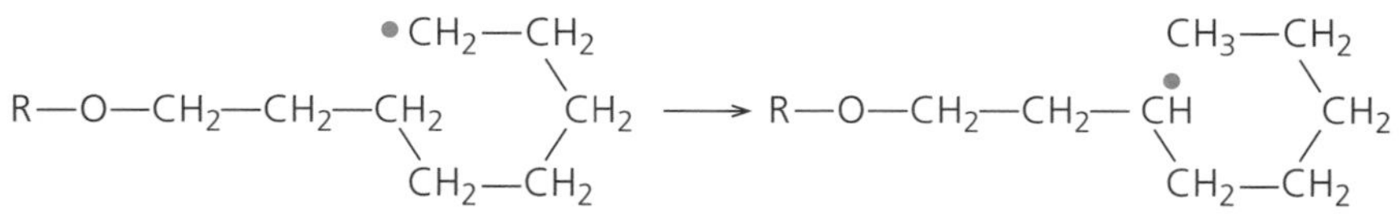

CHAIN TERMINATION

- Occurs when two radicals combine.

$$R{-}O{-}(CH_2)_n{-}CH_2{-}CH_2\bullet \ + \ R{-}O{-}(CH_2)_m{-}CH_2{-}CH_2\bullet$$
$$\downarrow$$
$$R{-}O{-}(CH_2)_n{-}CH_2{-}CH_2{-}CH_2{-}CH_2{-}(CH_2)_m{-}O{-}R$$

REPEATING UNIT

- **Repeating unit** shows the monomer with its π bond broken and 'continuation bonds' coming off each of the two carbon atoms that were π bonded.
- Polymer consists of thousands of these repeating units joined together . . . shown by the $_n$ at the end of the bracket.

- All the addition polymers in the table on the next page, except PTFE, have this repeating unit where R is:

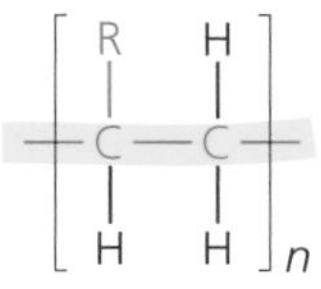

– H for poly(ethene)
– CH_3 for poly(propene)
– Cl for PVC
– C_6H_5 for polystyrene

Monomer	Name of polymer	Repeating unit	Uses
Ethene $CH_2{=}CH_2$	poly(ethene) (polythene)	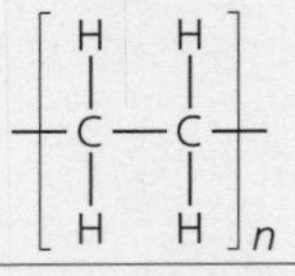	Plastic bags, cling film, dustbin liners, bottles
Propene $CH_2{=}CHCH_3$	poly(propene) (polypropylene)	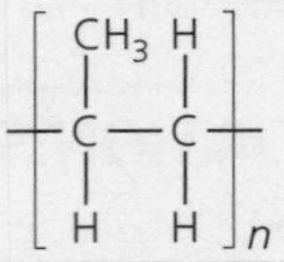	Ropes, car bumpers, carpet fibres
Chloroethene (vinylchloride) $CH_2{=}CHCl$	poly(chloroethene) PVC	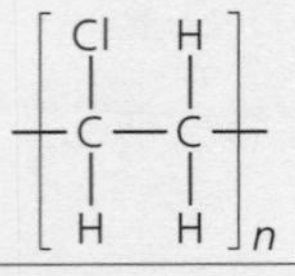	Window frames, gutters, water pipes, electrical insulation, fake leather clothing
Phenylethene (styrene) $CH_2{=}CHC_6H_5$	polystyrene	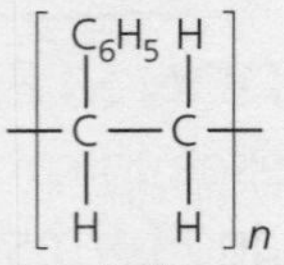	Mobile phones, thermal insulation, packaging
Tetrafluoroethene $CF_2{=}CF_2$	PTFE	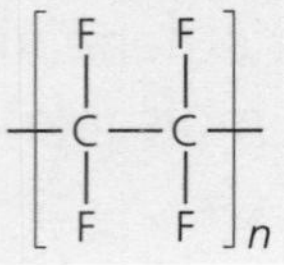	Non-stick pans, lining for breathable waterproof clothing (Gore-tex)

DISPOSAL

- All addition polymers are nonbiodegradable.
- Both an advantage – they do not rot – and a disadvantage – disposal.

LANDFILL

- They fill up landfill sites because they do not biodegrade.
- Landfill sites are getting harder to find.
- If dumped by the roadside, nonbiodegradable polymers cause an unsightly mess.

COMBUSTION

- Cause CO_2 omissions (global warming).
- Can cause toxic fumes such as dioxins (PVC also produces HCl).

GEOMETRY

start OCR only

- Monomers of formula CH_2CHR can form polymers with different relative arrangements of the R group along the chain.

ATACTIC

- Made by free radical polymerisation.
- CH_3 groups in poly(propene) are arranged randomly.

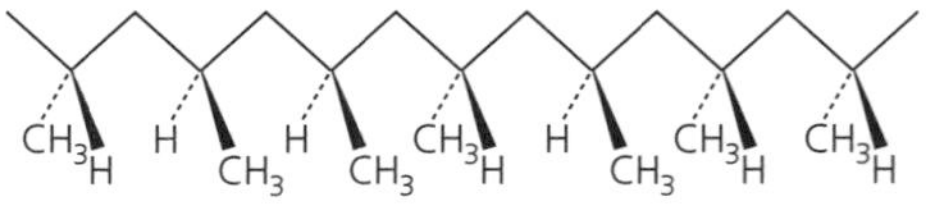

- Causes fewer van der Waals forces between adjacent chains... so the polymer has a low melting point and is not suitable for fibres.

ISOTACTIC

- Made from Ziegler–Natta catalysts.
- CH_3 groups in poly(propene) are all on the same side of the carbon chain.

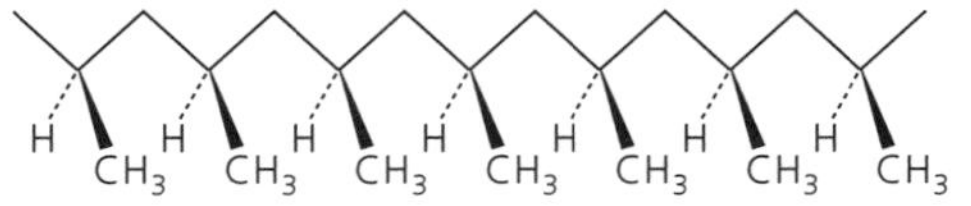

- The chains can lie parallel to each other . . . so the intermolecular forces are much stronger.
- Used for making car bumpers where strength is an important factor.

end OCR only

BENZENE

STRUCTURE OF BENZENE

- **Benzene** consists of six carbon atoms in a **planar hexagonal ring** with a hydrogen atom bonded to each carbon.
- Each carbon atom is joined by σ bonds to its neighbouring two carbon atoms and it is also bonded to the hydrogen atom by σ bond. This uses three of the carbon's electrons. The fourth valence electron is in a $2p_z$ orbital above and below the plane of the ring. This $2p_z$ electron overlaps with the $2p_z$ electrons of all the other carbon atoms in the ring, resulting in a **π bond system** above and below the ring.

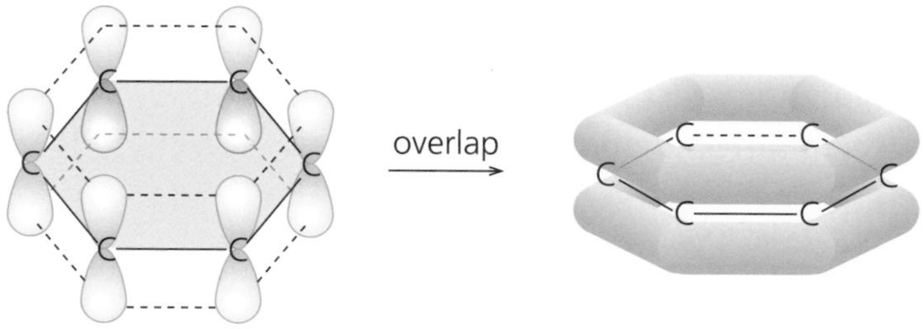

- These electrons are delocalised and give the benzene ring extra stability.
- The amount by which it is stabilised by resonance is called the **resonance stabilisation energy**.
- Because the benzene ring is not a system with alternating single and double bonds, the formula is usually written as 

MUST REMEMBER

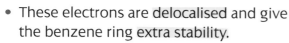

- There is a hydrogen atom on each of the six carbon atoms in benzene.

EVIDENCE FOR RESONANCE STABILISATION

- This compares the enthalpy changes concerning:
  - benzene, which has a delocalised π system
  - with a theoretical molecule, 'cyclohexatriene', which has six σ and six localised π bonds alternating around the ring.

ENTHALPY OF HYDROGENATION

- Cyclohexene has one double bond. Enthalpy change for the addition of hydrogen is given by:

- Enthalpy change for the hydrogenation of cyclohexa-1,4-diene is given by:

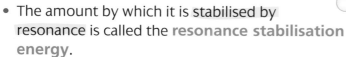

- Enthalpy change for the hydrogenation of the mythical 'cyclohexatriene' would be $3 \times -120 = -360\ \text{kJ mol}^{-1}$.
- Enthalpy change for the hydrogenation of benzene is less than this:

- The difference $360 - 208 = 152\ \text{kJ mol}^{-1}$ is the value of the resonance stabilisation energy.

MUST REMEMBER

- The **standard enthalpy of formation** of a compound is the enthalpy change when **1 mol** of it is made from its component elements in their **standard states under standard conditions** (1 atm or 101 kPa pressure and a temperature of 298K).

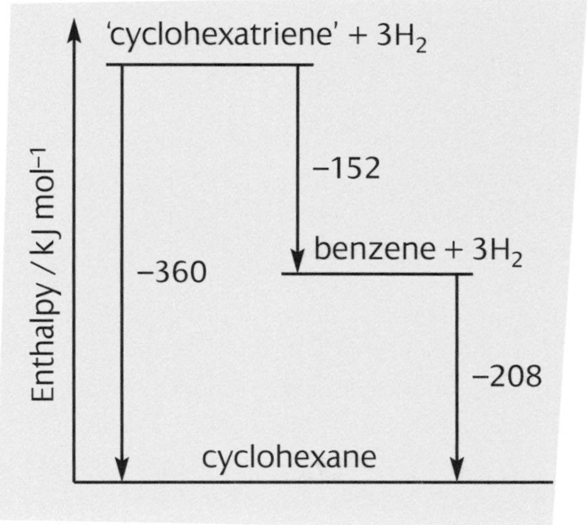

REACTIONS OF BENZENE

Because of the resonance stabilisation energy, most of benzene's reactions are electrophilic substitution reactions – unlike ethene which reacts by electrophilic addition reactions.

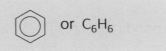

 or C_6H_6

NITRATION

- Benzene reacts with conc. nitric acid to form nitrobenzene and water:

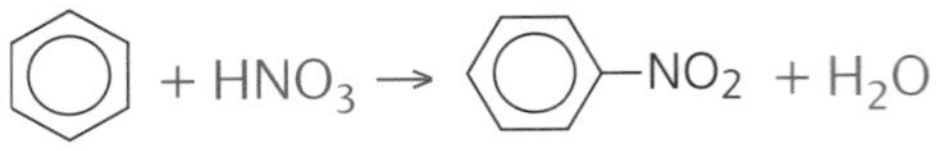

Conditions	**conc. H_2SO_4** catalyst temperature between 50°C and 60°C
Type of reaction	**electrophilic substitution**

HALOGENATION

- Benzene reacts with liquid bromine to form bromobenzene and hydrogen bromide:

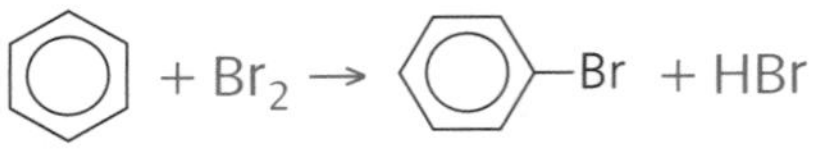

Conditions	**dry with iron or anhydrous $FeBr_3$ catalyst**
Type of reaction	**electrophilic substitution**

ALKYLATION

- This reaction is also called the **Friedel–Crafts reaction**.
- Benzene reacts with halogenoalkanes, such as chloroethane, to give ethylbenzene and hydrogen chloride:

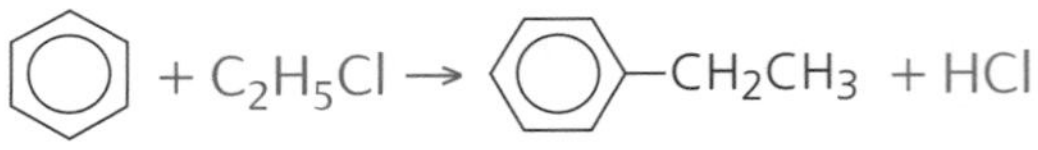

Conditions	**heat under reflux with anhydrous Al_2Cl_6 catalyst**
Type of reaction	**electrophilic substitution**

ACYLATION (not OCR)

- This is also an example of the Friedel–Crafts reaction.
- Benzene reacts with an acid chloride, such as ethanoyl chloride, to form a ketone, phenylethanone, and hydrogen chloride:

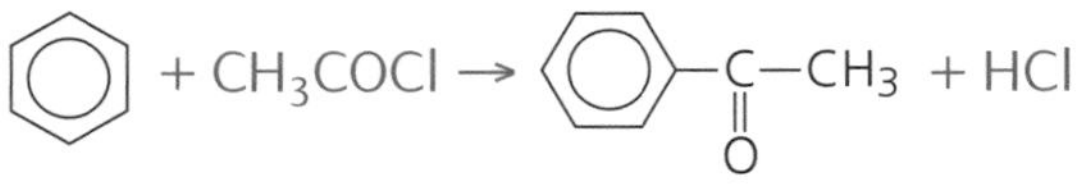

Conditions	**heat under reflux with anhydrous Al_2Cl_6 catalyst**
Type of reaction	**electrophilic substitution**

For practice in answering A2 Chemistry questions, why not use *Collins Do Brilliantly A2 Chemistry*?

SIDE CHAIN OXIDATION (Edexcel only)

Carbon containing side chains, such as the products of alkylation and acylation, can be oxidised by alkaline potassium manganate(VII) solutions to the salt of benzoic acid. The organic product is always the same regardless of the number of carbon atoms in the side chain:

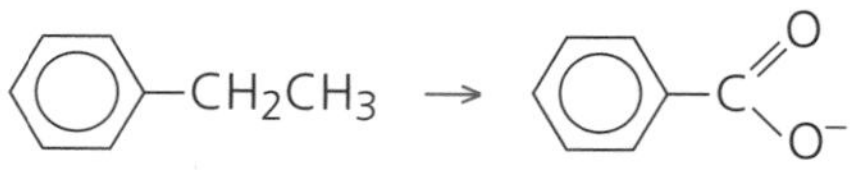

OTHER REACTIONS OF BENZENE

HYDROGENATION

- On heating with a platinum catalyst, benzene adds hydrogen and forms cyclohexane:
  $C_6H_6 + 3H_2 \rightarrow C_6H_{12}$

CHLORINATION

- On boiling in UV light, benzene adds chlorine and forms 1,2,3,4,5,6-hexachlorocyclohexane, $C_6H_6Cl_6$.

COMBUSTION

- Benzene burns in air with a smoky flame, producing carbon, CO, CO_2 and water vapour.

SUBSTITUTION VS ADDITION

SUBSTITUTION TO BENZENE

- The mechanism is that an electrophile adds on, but in a second step H^+ is lost in order to regain the stability of the benzene ring – the resonance stabilisation energy.
- This is energetically more favourable than adding another species in the second step – which is what happens with alkenes.

ADDITION TO ETHENE

- Alkenes add electrophiles because the π bond present is an area of high electron density.
- In the addition of HBr, the $\delta+$ H of HBr adds on as H^+.
- This is followed by the addition of Br^-.

PHENOL

start not AQA

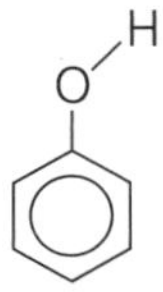

or C_6H_5OH

STRUCTURE

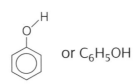

- **Phenol** contains an OH group as do alcohols, but as the oxygen atom is attached to a benzene ring its properties are significantly different.
- One of the lone pair of electrons on the oxygen atom is in the p_z orbital and so can overlap with the p_z electron in the carbon atom to which it is joined.
- This causes the delocalised π system to extend over the oxygen as well as around the ring.

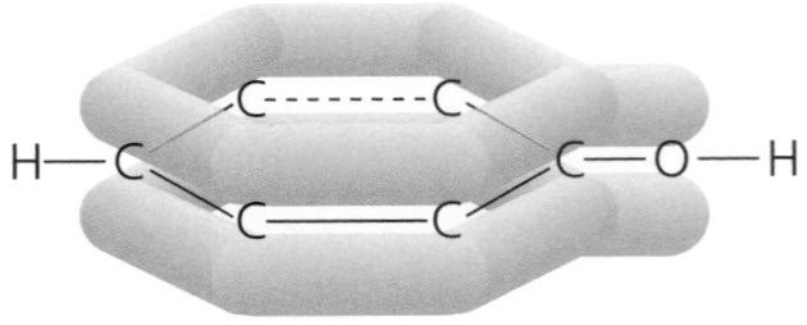

- Electrons are partially withdrawn from the oxygen atom into the ring. This has several effects.

ACIDITY

- The withdrawing of the electrons into the ring causes the H atom of the OH group to become more δ+ than in alcohols.
- Phenol is a strong enough acid to react with sodium hydroxide – whereas alcohols do not react with NaOH:
  $C_6H_5OH + NaOH \rightarrow C_6H_5O^-Na^+ + H_2O$
- Phenol, unlike carboxylic acids, is too weak to liberate CO_2 from carbonates or hydrogencarbonates:
  $C_6H_5OH + Na_2CO_3 \rightarrow$ no reaction

In reactions that do **not** involve substitution into the ring, it is easier to write the formula of phenol as C_6H_5OH rather than drawing it in full.

ELECTROPHILIC SUBSTITUTION

- Electron density in the ring is increased by the oxygen's lone pair, and so phenol will react more readily than benzene in electrophilic substitution reactions.
- It reacts rapidly with bromine water to form a precipitate of 2,4,6-tribromophenol:

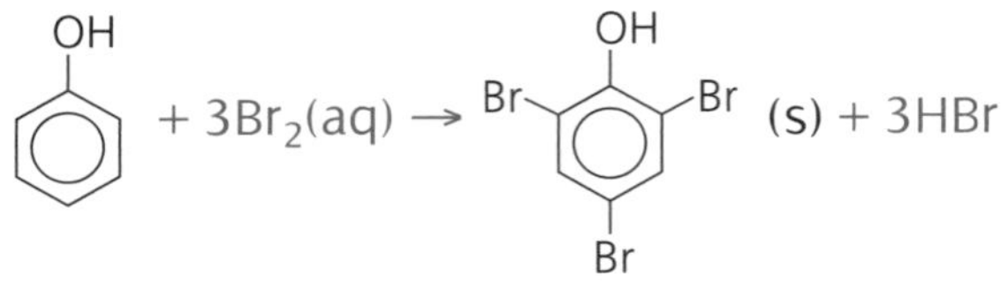

FORMATION OF AZO DYES

- When phenol, dissolved in alkali, is added to a solution containing diazonium ions, a bright yellow insoluble dye is formed.

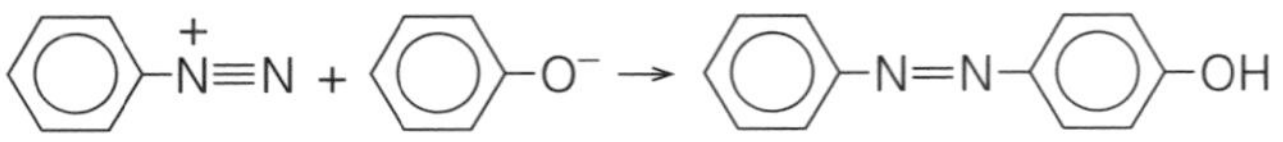

- Lone pairs on both nitrogen atoms act as a link forming delocalisation over both benzene rings, the two nitrogen atoms and the oxygen atom.
- This extended system causes the difference in energy levels around the N=N to be such that visible light is absorbed when one of the bonding electrons is promoted to a higher level.

ALCOHOL REACTIONS OF PHENOL

- Phenol is less reactive as an alcohol than ethanol.
  - Does not react with carboxylic acids in an esterification reaction:
    $C_6H_5OH + CH_3COOH \rightarrow$ no reaction
  - Reacts slowly with acid chlorides to form an ester:
    $C_6H_5OH + CH_3COCl \rightarrow CH_3COOC_6H_5 + HCl$
  - Does not give steamy fumes with PCl_5 as the reaction is very slow and incomplete.

C_6H_5OH
- $+ NaOH \rightarrow C_6H_5O^-Na^+$
- $+ Br_2(aq) \rightarrow C_6H_2Br_3$
- $+ C_6H_5N_2^+ \rightarrow C_6H_5–N=N–C_6H_4OH$
- $+ CH_3COCl \rightarrow CH_3COOC_6H_5$

end not AQA

PHENYLAMINE

start not Nuffield

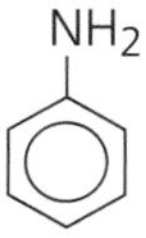

or $C_6H_5NH_2$

STRUCTURE

- The lone pair of electrons on the nitrogen atom becomes part of the delocalised π system of the benzene ring.
- The six π electrons of the carbon atoms and the lone pair from the nitrogen form a π system above and below the benzene ring.

PREPARATION

- **Phenylamine** is made by reducing nitrobenzene with tin and conc. HCl.
- Nitrobenzene, tin and conc. HCl are heated under reflux.
- After cooling, aqueous sodium hydroxide is added to release the phenylamine which is removed from the reaction mixture by steam distillation.

$$C_6H_5NO_2 + 6[H] + H^+ \rightarrow C_6H_5NH_3^+ + 2H_2O$$
$$C_6H_5NH_3^+ + OH^- \rightarrow C_6H_5NH_2 + H_2O$$

REACTIONS OF PHENYLAMINE

ELECTROPHILIC SUBSTITUTION

- The electron density in the ring is increased by the nitrogen's lone pair, and so phenylamine will react more readily than benzene in electrophilic substitution reactions.
- It reacts rapidly with bromine water to form a precipitate of 2,4,6-tribromophenylamine:

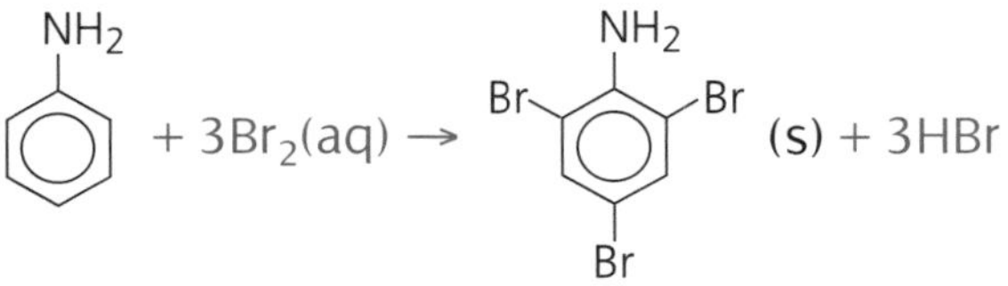

DIAZOTIZATION

- When dilute HCl and a solution of $NaNO_2$, sodium nitrate(III) (also called sodium nitrite), is carefully mixed with phenylamine and the temperature kept between 0°C and 5°C, a solution containing diazonium ions is formed:

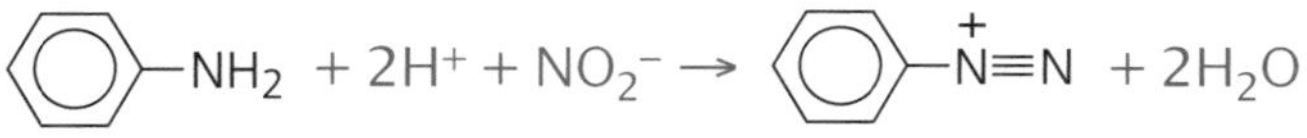

- If the temperature rises above 5°C, the diazonium ions decompose. If the temperature drops below 0°C, the reaction forming the ion is too slow.
- Diazonium ions are used to make azo dyes.

AS A BASE

- Because the lone pair of electrons on the nitrogen is partially drawn into the ring, phenylamine is a weaker base than ammonia. A solution of ammonia has a higher pH than a solution of phenylamine, but both react with acids:

$C_6H_5NH_2 + H^+ \rightarrow C_6H_5NH_3^+$ $NH_3 + H^+ \rightarrow NH_4^+$

In reactions that do **not** involve substitution into the ring, it is easier to write the formula of phenylamine as $C_6H_5NH_2$ rather than drawn out in full.

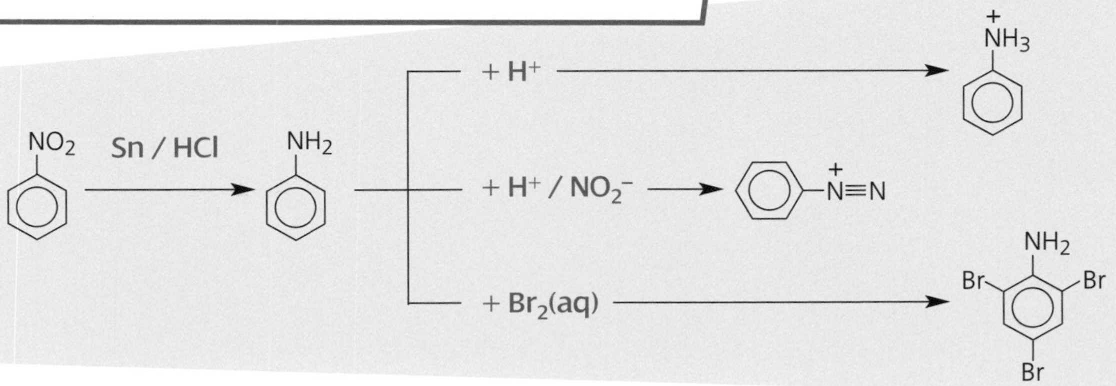

end not Nuffield

ETHYLAMINE / AMINOETHANE, $C_2H_5NH_2$

PHYSICAL PROPERTIES

- The nitrogen atom is $\delta-$ and the hydrogen atoms attached to it are $\delta+$.
- This causes **intermolecular hydrogen bonding** so the boiling point is higher than that of an alkane with a similar number of electrons.
- Amines are soluble in water because they can form hydrogen bonds with water molecules.

PREPARATION

REDUCTION OF NITRILES

- Nitriles, such as ethanenitrile, CH_3CN, can be reduced by lithium tetrahydridoaluminate, $LiAlH_4$, in dry ether solution:
  $CH_3C{\equiv}N + 4[H] \rightarrow CH_3CH_2NH_2$

FROM A HALOGENOALKANE

- If a halogenoalkane is mixed with excess conc. ammonia and left for several hours (or heated in a sealed tube), ethylamine is formed:
  $C_2H_5Cl + 2NH_3 \rightarrow C_2H_5NH_2 + NH_4Cl$
- The primary amine formed will react further with the halogenoalkane to form a secondary amine, and even a tertiary amine:
  $C_2H_5NH_2 + C_2H_5Cl \rightarrow (C_2H_5)_2NH + HCl$
- The HCl would then react with ammonia, forming NH_4Cl.

HOFMANN DEGRADATION REACTION (Edexcel only)

- When an amide such as ethanamide, CH_3CONH_2, is treated with liquid bromine and concentrated sodium hydroxide, an amine with one less carbon atom is formed:
  $CH_3CONH_2 + Br_2 + 4NaOH \rightarrow CH_3NH_2 + 2NaBr + Na_2CO_3 + 2H_2O$

REACTIONS OF ETHYLAMINE

- There is a lone pair of electrons on the nitrogen atom . . . so ethylamine can act as a base and as a nucleophile.

AS A BASE

- The ethyl group pushes electrons slightly towards the nitrogen and so ethylamine is a stronger base than ammonia, which, in turn, is stronger than phenylamine due to the electron withdrawing effect of the benzene ring.

	K_b / mol dm^{-3}
ethylamine	5.4×10^{-4}
ammonia	1.8×10^{-5}
phenylamine	5.0×10^{-10}

- Ethylamine reacts reversibly with water to produce an alkaline solution:
  $C_2H_5NH_2 + H_2O \rightleftharpoons C_2H_5NH_3^+ + OH^-$
- It reacts with acids:
  $C_2H_5NH_2 + H^+ \rightarrow C_2H_5NH_3^+$
  or $C_2H_5NH_2 + HCl \rightarrow C_2H_5NH_3Cl$
  as does ammonia:
  $NH_3 + H^+ \rightarrow NH_4^+$
  or $NH_3 + HCl \rightarrow NH_4Cl$

AS A NUCLEOPHILE

- Amines react with:
  - Halogenoalkanes
    They form a mixture of secondary and tertiary amines:
    $C_2H_5NH_2 + C_2H_5Cl \rightarrow (C_2H_5)_2NH + HCl$
    $(C_2H_5)_2NH + C_2H_5Cl \rightarrow (C_2H_5)_3N + HCl$
  - Acyl chlorides
    Amines react rapidly to form a substituted amide:
    $C_2H_5NH_2 + CH_3COCl$
    $\rightarrow CH_3CONH(C_2H_5) + HCl$

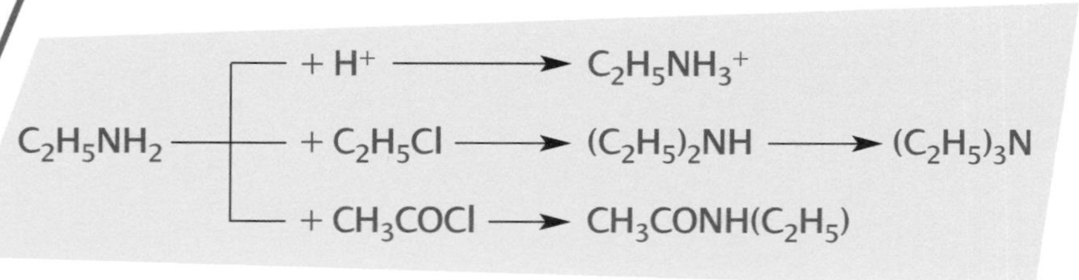

AMINO ACIDS

- **Amino acids** contain an NH_2 group and a COOH group.
- All naturally-occurring amino acids are α-amino acids – the NH_2 group and the COOH group are attached to the same carbon atom. They all have the same general formula that is shown on the right.

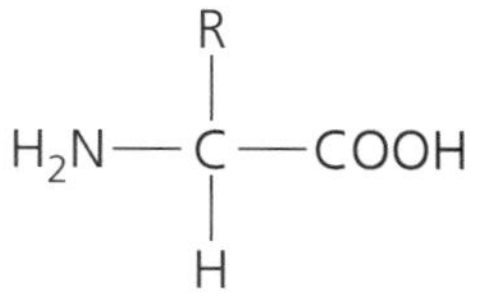

PHYSICAL PROPERTIES

MELTING POINT

- Amino acids are solids at room temperature because the acidic COOH group protonates the basic NH_2 group forming a species which has both a + and a – charge.

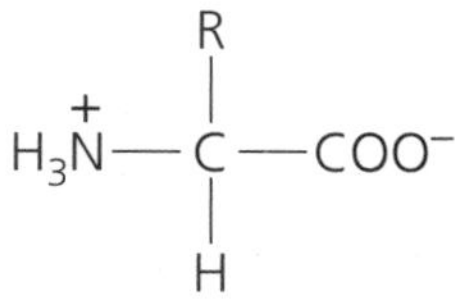

- This is called a **zwitterion** (from the German for hybrid or mongrel).
- The positive charge on one zwitterion is strongly attracted by the negative charge on another zwitterion, and so the amino acid is a solid.

SOLUBILITY

- Because of the two ionic charges, amino acids are soluble in water. The hydration of the + charge by the δ– oxygen atoms in water and the hydration of the – charge by the δ+ hydrogen atoms in the water are both exothermic.

REACTIONS OF AMINO ACIDS

+ ACID

- NH_2 group reacts as a base:
  $H_2NCH(CH_3)COOH + H^+$
  $\rightarrow H_3N^+CH(CH_3)COOH$
- This equation can also be written with the zwitterion reacting:
  $H_3N^+CH(CH_3)COO^- + H^+$
  $\rightarrow H_3N^+CH(CH_3)COOH$

+ ALKALI

- COOH group acts as an acid:
  $H_2NCH(CH_3)COOH + OH^-$
  $\rightarrow H_2NCH(CH_3)COO^- + H_2O$
- This equation can also be written with the zwitterion reacting:
  $H_3N^+CH(CH_3)COO^- + OH^-$
  $\rightarrow H_2NCH(CH_3)COO^- + H_2O$

PROTEIN FORMATION

- Enzymes will cause amino acids to polymerise into long chains with different amino acids joined by peptide links.

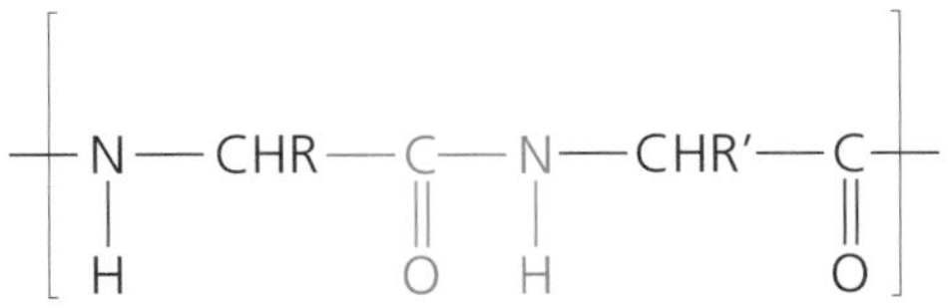

NITRILES

start

Edexcel and Nuffield only

- **Nitriles** contain the C≡N group.
- They are named after the longest carbon chain including the C of the CN group.
- CH_3CN is called ethanenitrile.

PREPARATION

NUCLEOPHILIC SUBSTITUTION

- Nitriles can be prepared by the nucleophilic substitution of KCN with halogenoalkanes.
- KCN in aqueous ethanol will react with a halogenoalkane.
- For example:
  $KCN + C_2H_5Br \rightarrow C_2H_5CN + KBr$

NUCLEOPHILIC ADDITION

- Nitriles can also be prepared by the nucleophilic addition of HCN to carbonyl compounds.
- For example:
  $HCN + CH_3CHO \rightarrow CH_3CH(OH)CN$

REACTIONS OF NITRILES

HYDROLYSIS BY ACID OR ALKALI

- Nitriles are hydrolysed to carboxylic acids by boiling under reflux with aqueous acid, or to the salt of a carboxylic acid by boiling under reflux with aqueous alkali:
  $CH_3CN + 2H_2O + H^+ \rightarrow CH_3COOH + NH_4^+$
  $CH_3CN + H_2O + OH^- \rightarrow CH_3COO^- + NH_3$

REDUCTION

- Nitriles are reduced to amines by lithium tetrahydridoaluminate, $LiAlH_4$:
  $CH_3CN + 4[H] \rightarrow CH_3CH_2NH_2$

end

Edexcel and Nuffield only

MECHANISMS

A curly arrow must:
- **start on a bond** and go towards an atom making a bond or an ion

or
- **start on a lone pair** of electrons on an atom and go towards another atom making a bond.

DEFINITIONS

- **A nucleophile is a species with a lone pair of electrons which it uses to form a covalent bond. It attacks a δ+ site.**
- **An electrophile is a species that accepts a pair of electrons forming a covalent bond. It attacks a δ– or electron rich site.**
- **A curly arrow represents the movement of a pair of electrons.**

FREE RADICAL SUBSTITUTION

ALKANES

- Alkanes, such as methane, react with chlorine and bromine in the presence of white or UV light in a **substitution reaction**. The mechanism involves **homolytic fission** of σ bonds.

$CH_4 + Cl_2 \rightarrow CH_3Cl + HCl$

Homolytic fission is where a bond breaks, with one of the bonding electrons going to one atom and the other going to the other atom. Two free radicals are formed:

$A–B \rightarrow A\cdot + B\cdot$

Initiation step

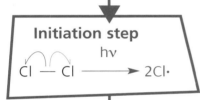

$Cl—Cl \xrightarrow{h\nu} 2Cl\cdot$

Propagation steps

The chlorine radical then pulls off an H atom from the methane molecule and a $CH_3\cdot$ radical is formed:

$CH_4 + Cl\cdot \rightarrow HCl + CH_3\cdot$

This then pulls off a Cl atom from a Cl_2 molecule, forming the organic product and another $Cl\cdot$ radical:

$CH_3\cdot + Cl_2 \rightarrow CH_3Cl + Cl\cdot$

Termination (chain breaking) steps

When two radicals meet they form a molecule and so break the chain reaction:

$CH_3\cdot + CH_3\cdot \rightarrow C_2H_6$

$Cl\cdot + Cl\cdot \rightarrow Cl_2$

$CH_3\cdot + Cl\cdot \rightarrow CH_3Cl$

NUCLEOPHILIC SUBSTITUTION

HALOGENOALKANES

- The δ+ carbon atom is attacked by nucleophiles such as OH^-, ^-CN and NH_3.
- The lone pair of electrons on the nucleophile (the oxygen of OH^-, the carbon of ^-CN or the nitrogen of NH_3) attacks the δ+ carbon atom. As the new bond forms, the C–halogen bond breaks.

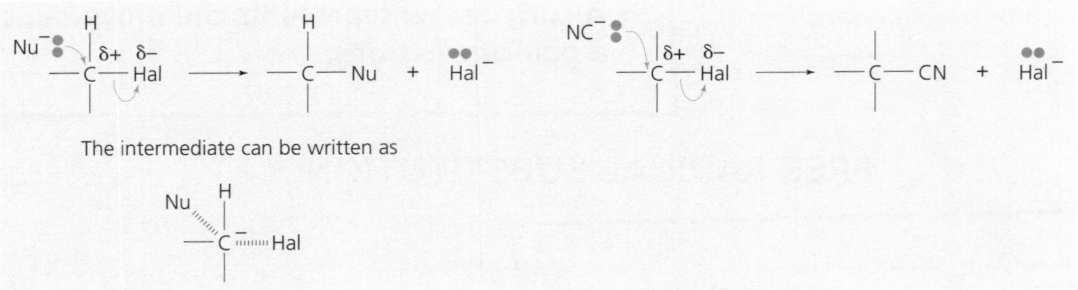

- This is known as an **S_N2 mechanism** – **S**ubstitution **N**ucleophilic **2**nd order.

S_N1 mechanism (Edexcel only)

- With tertiary, and some secondary, halogenoalkanes, a different mechanism is observed.
- The σ bond breaks forming the halide ion and a carbocation. This then accepts a pair of electrons from the nucleophile.

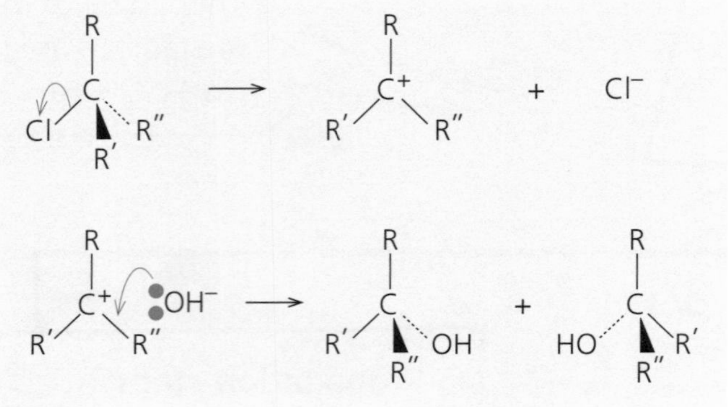

- This mechanism is called an **S_N1 mechanism** as the total order is 1; the partial order of the halogenoalkane is 1 and that of the nucleophile zero.

ACYL CHLORIDES (not OCR)

- These react in an **addition–elimination** reaction. The net result is the substitution of the chlorine atom by a nucleophile.
- Ethanoyl chloride reacts with water, alcohols, ammonia and amines in this way.
- The general mechanism is:

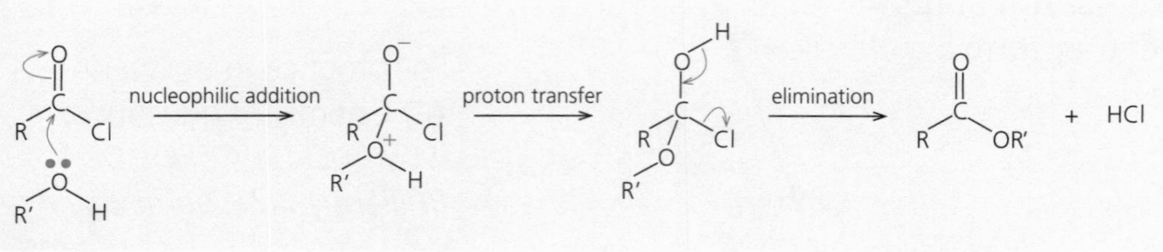

- Acyl chlorides are more reactive than carboxylic acids, because the C–Cl bond in the acyl chloride is weaker than the C–OH bond in the carboxylic acid.
- This makes the elimination step more energetically feasible.

ELECTROPHILIC SUBSTITUTION

BENZENE RING

- **Benzene** and other aromatic substances, such as phenol, react with **electrophiles**.
- The stability caused by the delocalised π system in the benzene ring, compared to the reactivity of the localised π bond in ethene, requires the production of a positively charged ion as the electrophile.
- The electrophile E^+ accepts a pair of electrons from benzene's π system forming a **carbocation**.
- However, unlike ethene, which adds a negative ion in step 2 (see 'Electrophilic addition', page 84), the benzene's intermediate loses an H^+ ion, so that the stability of the benzene ring is regained.
- The general mechanism is:

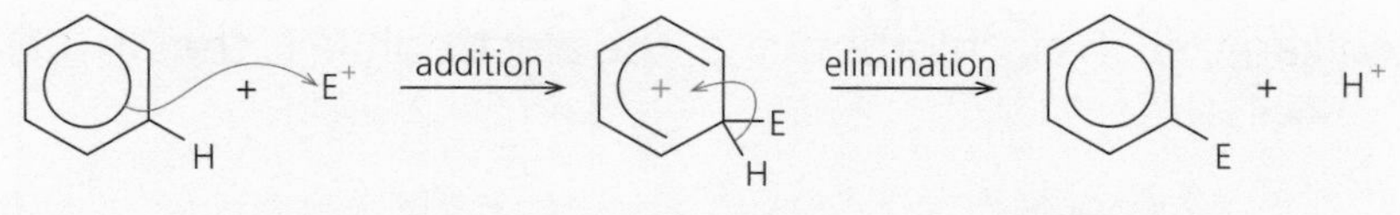

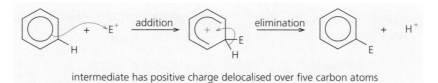

intermediate has positive charge delocalised over five carbon atoms

NITRATION

- Conditions: heat benzene, concentrated nitric acid and concentrated sulphuric acid under reflux at 50°C.
- In **nitration**, the electrophile is the NO_2^+ ion which is created by the reaction between the nitric acid and the catalyst, concentrated sulphuric acid. The H_2SO_4 is a stronger acid than HNO_3 and so protonates it:

  $HNO_3 + H_2SO_4 \rightarrow H_2NO_3^+ + HSO_4^-$
- The $H_2NO_3^+$ ion then loses H_2O forming the electrophile:
  $H_2NO_3^+ \rightarrow H_2O + NO_2^+$
- The NO_2^+ ion attacks the benzene ring, the positive intermediate loses a proton and nitrobenzene is formed.

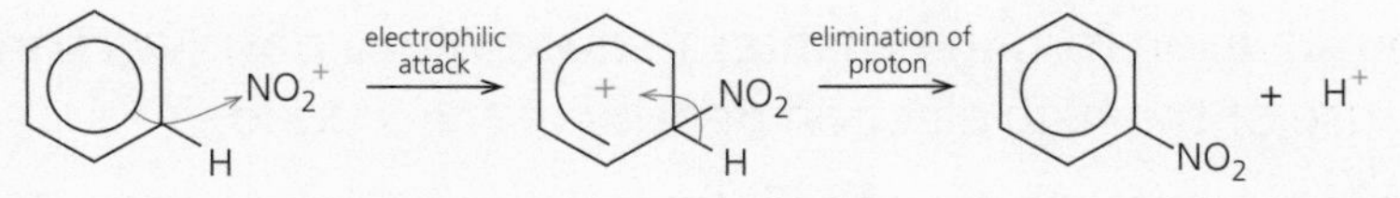

- A higher temperature would cause two NO_2 groups to be substituted.
- A lower temperature would cause the reaction to be too slow.

- The water produced is protonated by another H_2SO_4 molecule so the overall reaction is:
  $HNO_3 + 2H_2SO_4 \rightarrow NO_2^+ + 2HSO_4^- + H_3O^+$

BROMINATION

- Conditions: dry benzene and liquid bromine refluxed in the presence of iron filings or anhydrous $FeBr_3$ catalyst.
- In **bromination**, the electrophile is the Br^+ ion.
- The iron reacts with some of the bromine to form $FeBr_3$. This then reacts with more bromine to form the electrophile: $FeBr_3 + Br_2 \rightarrow Br^+ + FeBr_4^-$

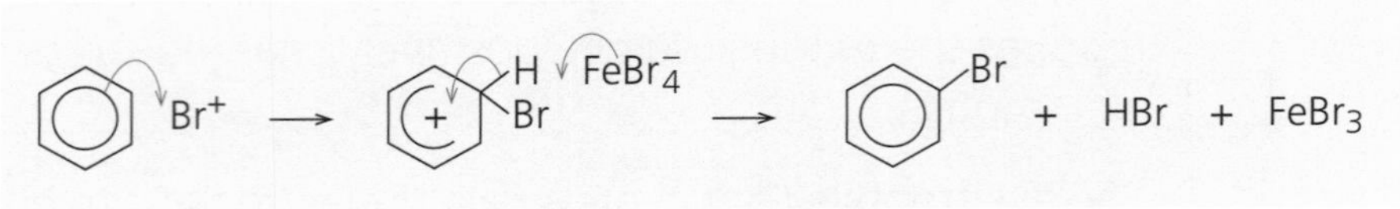

FRIEDEL–CRAFTS REACTION

- Benzene reacts with halogenoalkanes (required by all exam boards) and with acyl chlorides (not OCR).
- Conditions: a catalyst of anhydrous aluminium chloride.
- With a halogenoalkane, such as chloroethane, the electrophile is the $CH_3CH_2^+$ ion: $CH_3CH_2Cl + AlCl_3 \rightarrow CH_3CH_2^+ + AlCl_4^-$

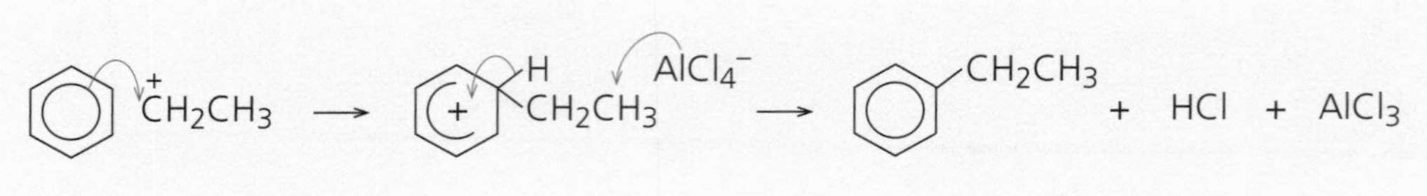

- With an acyl chloride, such as ethanoyl chloride, the electrophile is $CH_3C^+{=}O$: $CH_3COCl + AlCl_3 \rightarrow CH_3C^+{=}O + AlCl_4^-$

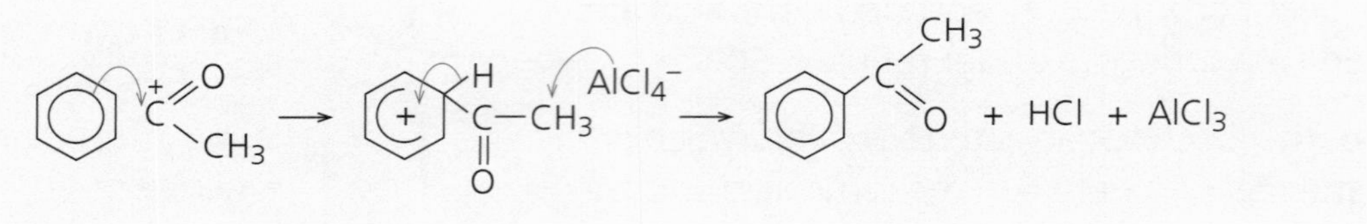

ELECTROPHILIC ADDITION

ALKENES

- Alkenes react by this mechanism with hydrogen halides, chlorine and bromine.
- The first step is the addition of a positive ion forming an intermediate with a positive charge on a carbon atom. This works because of the high electron density of the π bond.
- The second step is the formation of a σ bond between the intermediate and the negative ion.

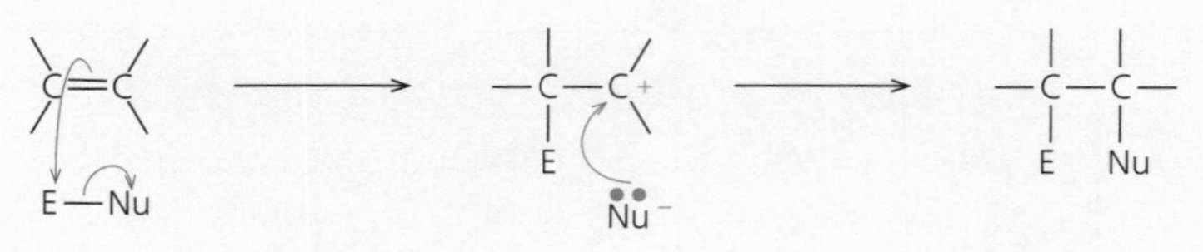

- The addition of HBr to an asymmetrical alkene, such as propene, could produce two isomers:

$CH_2{=}CHCH_3 + HBr \rightarrow CH_3CHBrCH_3$

$CH_2{=}CHCH_3 + HBr \rightarrow CH_2BrCH_2CH_3$

- The reason that 2-bromopropane is the major product is that the secondary carbocation **intermediate**, $CH_3C^+HCH_3$, is more stable than the primary carbocation $C^+H_2CH_2CH_3$.
- This explains **Markovnikov's rule** – **in the addition of HX to an asymmetric alkene, the H atom goes to the carbon which already has more H atoms directly bonded to it.**

ADDITION OF A HYDROGEN HALIDE

- Conditions: mix the alkene and the gaseous hydrogen halide.

  $CH_2{=}CH_2 + HBr \rightarrow CH_3CH_2Br$
- HBr is polarised with the hydrogen atom δ+. This is the electrophile.

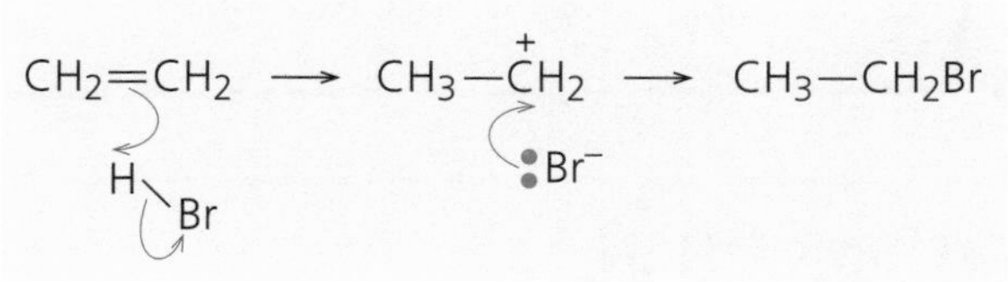

- The intermediate carbocation is planar, as the carbon atom has three bond pairs and no lone pairs of electrons around it. The addition of HBr to both *cis*- and *trans*- but-2-ene gives the racemic mixture of the 2-bromobutane as the Br^- can attack from either above or below the plane of the molecule.

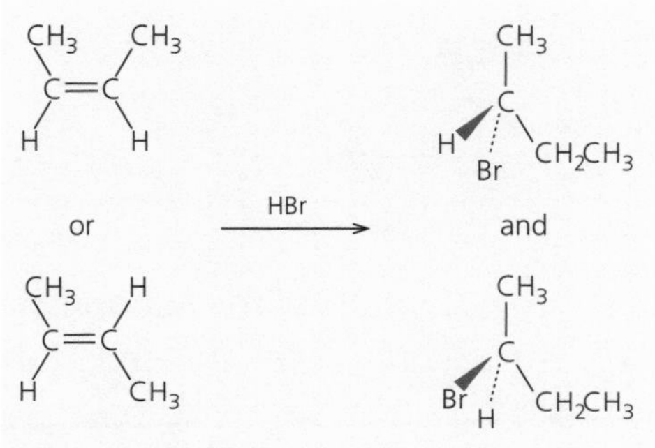

ADDITION OF HALOGEN

- Conditions: bubble the alkene into bromine liquid or bromine dissolved in a solvent such as hexane.

  $CH_2{=}CH_2 + Br_2 \rightarrow CH_2BrCH_2Br$
- As a halogen molecule, such as Br_2, approaches the π bond in an alkene, it becomes polarised by the high electron density in the π bond. This causes the Br atom nearer to the alkene to become δ+ and this is the electrophile.

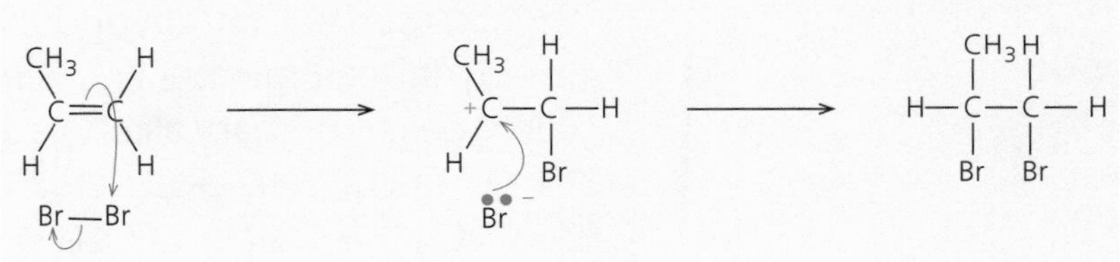

ADDITION OF SULPHURIC ACID (AQA only)

- Conditions: bubble the alkene into cold concentrated sulphuric acid and then add water to hydrolyse the product.

  $CH_2{=}CH_2 + H_2SO_4 \rightarrow CH_3CH_2(HSO_4)$ $CH_3CH_2(HSO_4) + H_2O \rightarrow CH_3CH_2OH + H_2SO_4$
- The δ+ hydrogen in sulphuric acid is the electrophile.

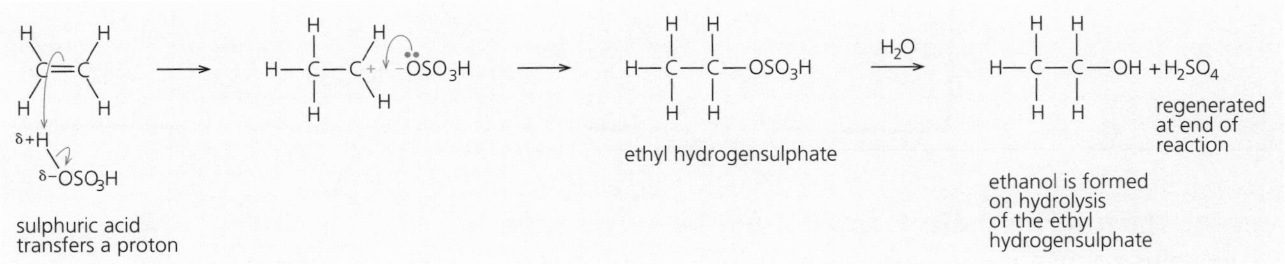

NUCLEOPHILIC ADDITION

ALDEHYDES AND KETONES

- Both contain the **carbonyl group**, C=O. Oxygen is more electronegative than carbon and so the double bond is polarised and the carbon atom becomes δ+. This causes it to be attacked by nucleophiles.

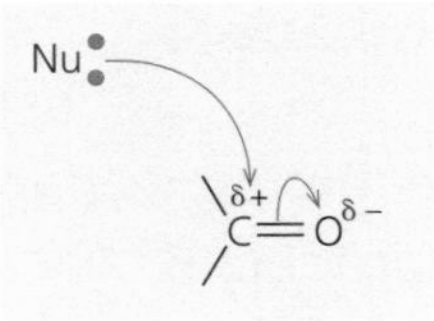

ADDITION OF HCN

- Conditions: mix the aldehyde or ketone with a mixture of HCN and KCN, or either, but buffered at pH = 8.
- HCN is not a nucleophile but ⁻CN ions are. In the first step, the mechanism requires ⁻CN ions which attack the carbonyl group.
- In the second step, the mechanism requires HCN molecules. In this step the proton bonds to the oxygen.

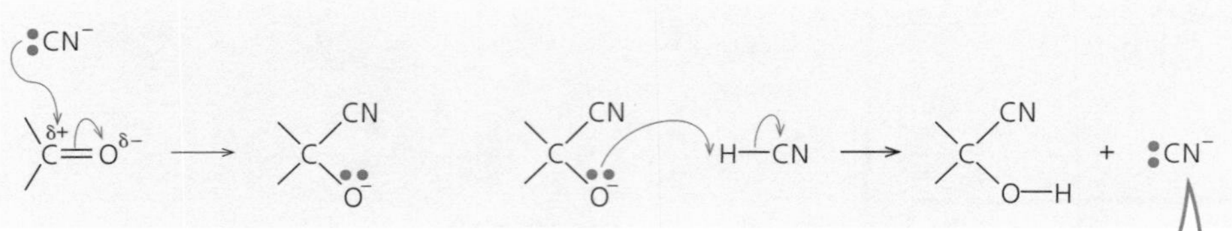

- The ⁻CN ions are regenerated in the second step and so they act as the catalyst for this reaction.

> - If the pH is too low, there are not enough ⁻CN ions for the 1st step.
> - If it is too high, there are not enough HCN molecules for the 2nd step.

NUCLEOPHILIC REDUCTION

- Aqueous sodium tetrahydridoborate(III), $NaBH_4$, or lithium tetrahydridoaluminate(III), $LiAlH_4$, in dry ether solution will reduce aldehydes to primary alcohols and ketones to secondary alcohols:
  $CH_3CH_2CHO + 2[H] \rightarrow CH_3CH_2CH_2OH$
  $CH_3COCH_3 + 2[H] \rightarrow CH_3CH(OH)CH_3$
- The mechanism is attack by H⁻ ions from the reducing agent.
- The O⁻ then removes a proton from a water molecule.

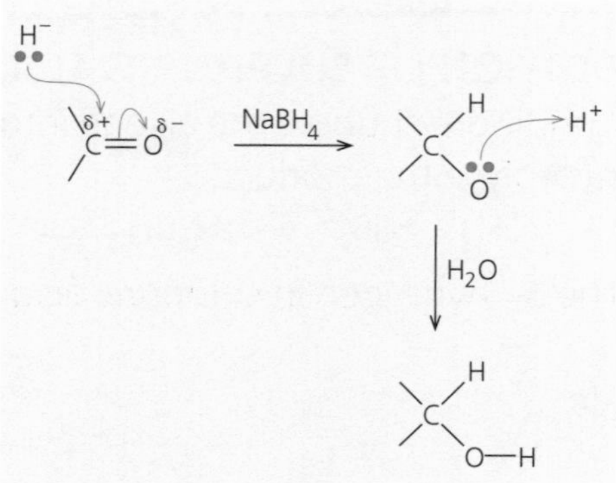

> - When lithium tetrahydridoaluminate(III) is used as the reducing agent, the **intermediate formed must be subsequently hydrolysed** by adding aqueous acid, such as dilute HCl.

KEY POINTS

FREE RADICAL SUBSTITUTION
Alkanes + halogens

NUCLEOPHILIC SUBSTITUTION
Halogenoalkanes + OH^- from NaOH(aq)
+ ^-CN from KCN
+ NH_3 in aqueous ethanol solvent

Acyl chlorides (not OCR) + H_2O
+ alcohols, such as C_2H_5OH
+ NH_3
+ amines such as $C_2H_5NH_2$

ELECTROPHILIC SUBSTITUTION
Benzene + HNO_3
+ Br_2
+ halogenoalkanes, such as C_2H_5Br
+ acyl chlorides, such as CH_3COCl (not OCR)

ELECTROPHILIC ADDITION
Alkenes + HBr (and all other hydrogen halides)
+ Br_2 (and Cl_2 but not I_2)
+ H_2SO_4 followed by water (AQA only)

NUCLEOPHILIC ADDITION
Aldehydes and ketones + HCN (in the presence of KCN)
+ H^- (from $NaBH_4$ or $LiAlH_4$)

SPECTRAL ANALYSIS

MASS SPECTRA

IONISATION AND FRAGMENTATION

- In a mass spectrometer, the substance under test is bombarded with high-energy electrons. These ionise the molecule by knocking off an electron:
  $M(g) + e^- \rightarrow M^+(g) + 2e^-$
- The M^+ ion is called the molecular ion and will have the highest *m/e* value in the spectrum, but some of these ions fragment into an ion with a smaller *m/e* value and a radical. For example:
  $CH_3COCH_3^+ \rightarrow CH_3CO^+ + CH_3\cdot$

IDENTIFICATION OF PEAKS

- Peaks are often observed with values of 15 less than the molecular ion peak due to the loss of CH_3. A value of M-29 is caused by the loss of $C_2H_5\cdot$ and one at M-43 by the loss of $CH_3CO\cdot$.
- The peaks are caused by positive ions such as:

ion M^+	*m/e* M_r value
CH_3^+	15
$C_2H_5^+$	29
CHO^+	29
$C_3H_7^+$	43
CH_3CO^+	43

There is sometimes a tiny peak at an *m/e* value of one more than the molecular ion peak. This M +1 peak is caused by the slight amount of the ^{13}C isotope in the molecule. The relative height of this peak to the molecular ion peak indicates the number of carbon atoms in the molecule.

The mass spectrum of ethanol

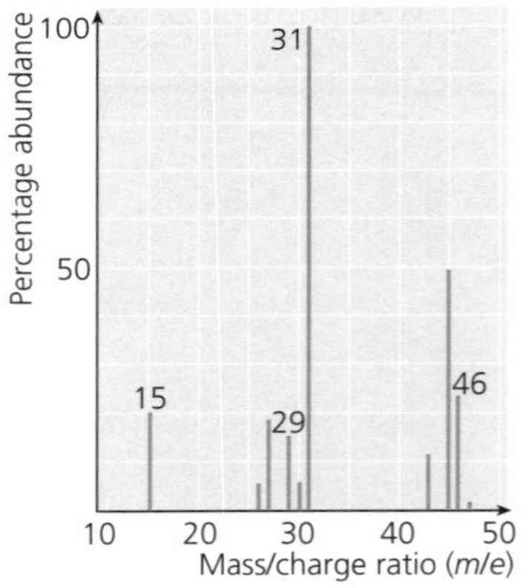

The peaks are:

m/e = 46 $C_2H_5OH^+$ (the molecular ion)
m/e = 31 CH_2OH^+ (loss of 15)
m/e = 29 $CH_3CH_2^+$
m/e = 15 CH_3^+

The mass spectrum of butane

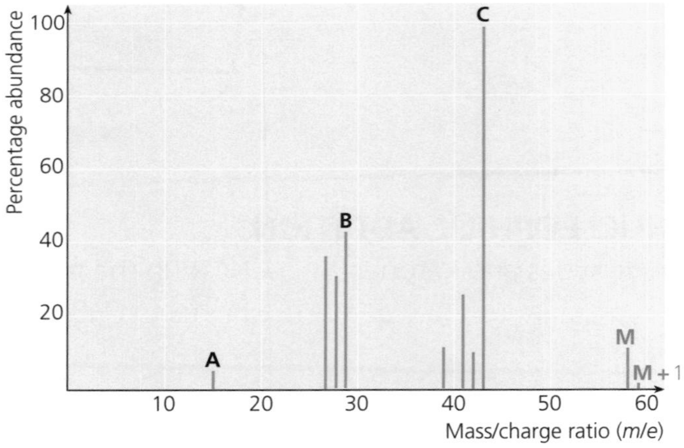

The peaks are:

M	*m/e* = 58	$C_4H_{10}^+$
C	*m/e* = 43	$C_3H_7^+$
B	*m/e* = 29	$C_2H_5^+$
A	*m/e* = 15	CH_3^+

INFRARED SPECTRA

CAUSES

- The molecules absorb infrared light energy and the vibrations of the molecules increase. These vibrations can be either **bond stretching** or **bending** and result in a change in dipole moment of the molecule.
- **Polar** molecules such as H_2O and molecules with polar bonds such as CO_2 absorb infrared radiation. The latter are greenhouse gases in the earth's atmosphere because they absorb some of the infrared radiated by the warm earth back towards space.
- The bonds in N_2 and O_2 are **non-polar** so they do not absorb infrared radiation. This means they are not greenhouse gases.

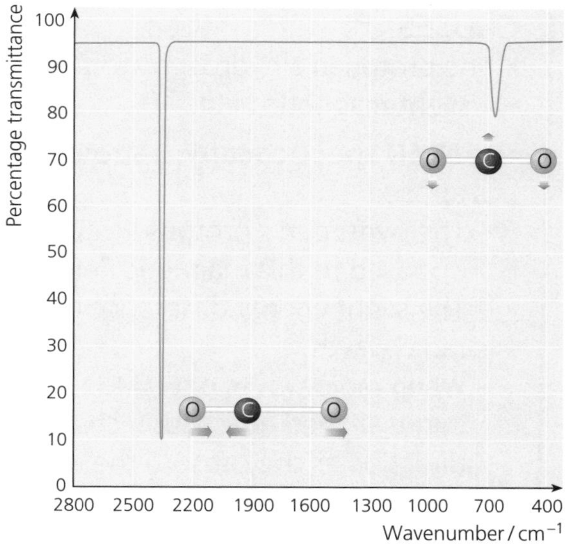

Infrared spectrum of CO_2 showing the vibrations that cause absorption

CHARACTERISTIC FREQUENCIES

- The frequency is proportional to the **wavenumber** in cm^{-1}, which is defined as 1/wavelength. This is a more convenient unit than the actual frequency.
- The stretching of the O–H bond in alcohols and carboxylic acids causes a broad peak around a wave number of 3300 cm^{-1}. This is broad because of hydrogen bonding.
- Another important peak is that around 1700 cm^{-1} which is caused by the stretching of the C=O bond in aldehydes, ketones, acids and acid derivatives such as esters.

Bond		Range of wavenumber /cm^{-1}
N–H	Amines	3350 – 3500
O–H	Hydrogen bonded in alcohols Hydrogen bonded in carboxylic acids	3230 – 3550 2500 – 3300
C–H	Alkanes and alkenes	2840 – 3030
C=O	Aldehydes, ketones, acids and acid derivatives	1680 – 1750
C=C	Alkenes	1610 – 1680
C–O	Alcohols, acids and esters	1000 – 1300

- Don't need to learn these values because they will be given in the exam.
- But should know where to look in the spectrum for evidence of a C=O bond and an O–H bond.

Infrared spectrum of ethanoic acid

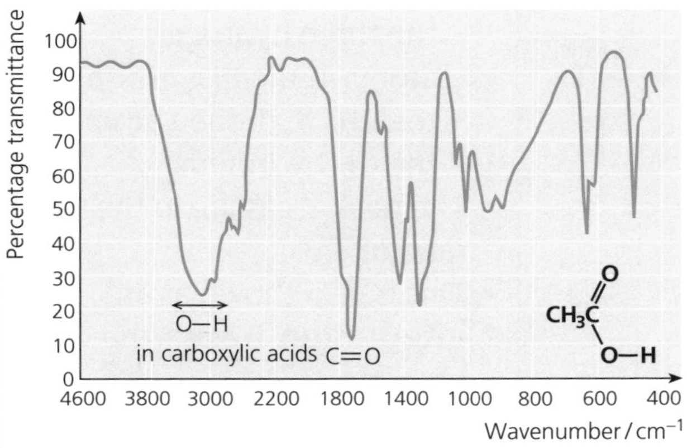

Infrared spectrum of ethanol

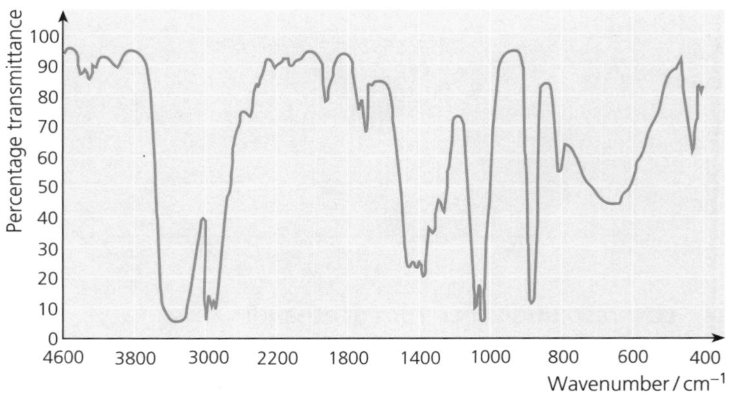

NUCLEAR MAGNETIC RESONANCE (NMR) SPECTRA

CAUSES

- The proton in a hydrogen atom is spinning and so causes a slight magnetic field.
- In **NMR spectroscopy**, a strong external magnetic field is applied:
  - The hydrogen's protons lie either aligned with or opposed to this magnetic field.
  - The slight energy difference is equal to the energy of radio waves.
  - When radio waves of 60 MHz are applied, the protons in the aligned orientation change to the opposed direction as they absorb the radio waves.
  - The energy difference, ΔE, between the two states depends on the chemical environment of the hydrogen atoms in the molecule and the strength of the applied magnetic field.

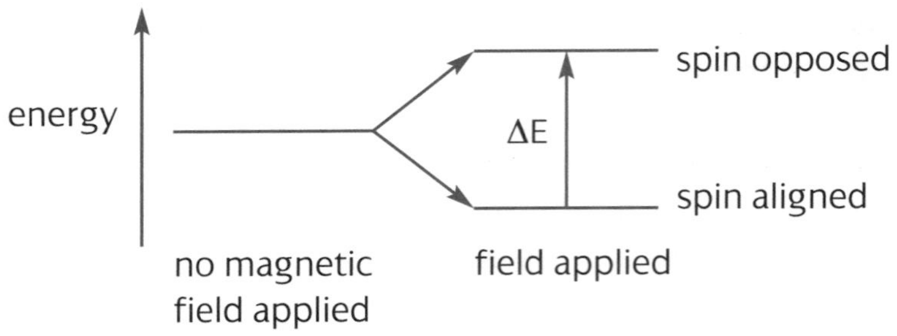

- It is the hydrogen **atoms not the groups**, **nor the bonds** that cause the NMR spectrum.
- Hydrogen's isotope, deuterium, does not give lines in the spectrum.

LOW-RESOLUTION NMR

- Hydrogen nuclei in different chemical environments will have different values of ΔE. These are measured relative to a standard which are the hydrogen atoms in TMS, tetramethylsilane, $Si(CH_3)_4$. The chemical shift is given the symbol δ.
- The area under the peaks at each δ value is proportional to the number of hydrogen atoms in that chemical environment.

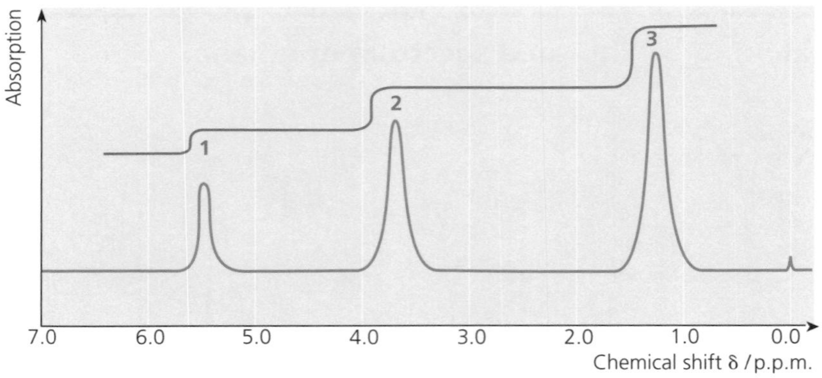

Low-resolution spectrum of ethanol

- Ethanol, CH_3CH_2OH, has three peaks due to:
  - the three hydrogen atoms in the CH_3 group
  - the CH_2 hydrogen atoms
  - the OH hydrogen.
- The peak areas are in the ratio of 3:2:1.
- This is also shown as an **integration trace** – the blue line.

ANALYSIS OF NMR SPECTRA

- The values of the chemical shifts and the integrated peak areas can be used to find the structure of the organic compound.

Group	δ / ppm	Group	δ / ppm
R–CH_3	0.8 – 1.2	R–OH	1.0 – 6.0
R–CH_2–R	1.1 – 1.5	R–CH_2–OH	3.3 – 4.0
R_3CH	1.5	R_2CHOH	3.2 – 4.1
C_6H_5–H	7.1 – 7.5	C_6H_5–CH_2–R	2.3 – 2.7
C_6H_5–CH_3	2.1 – 2.5	R–CH_2Cl	3.2 – 3.7

- The values of chemical shifts will be given in the exam.
- Must remember that the hydrogen in OH can have δ values that vary enormously.

- A compound with a molecular formula of C_8H_{10} has the NMR spectrum:

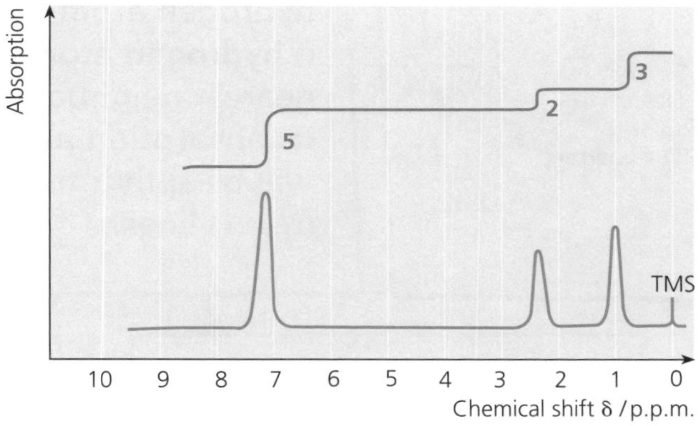

  - The peak at δ = 7.2 is caused by H atoms on a benzene ring. This has a relative intensity of 5, so there must be five hydrogen atoms attached to the benzene ring.
  - The peak at δ = 2.4 is caused by the H atoms in a CH_2 group or in a CH_3 group attached to a benzene ring, but its relative intensity is 2, so it must be due to the CH_2 hydrogen atoms.
  - The peak at δ = 1.0 is caused by the H atoms in a CH_3 group not on a benzene ring.
- The substance is:

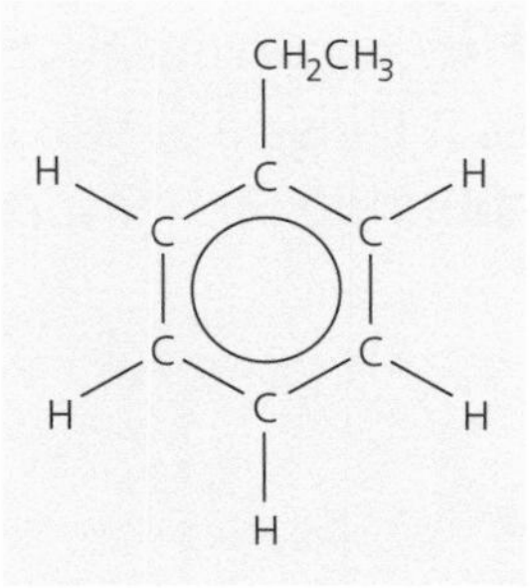

SPIN COUPLING – HIGH RESOLUTION NMR

start AQA and OCR only

SPIN–SPIN SPLITTING

- If a **high-resolution spectrometer** is used, it will be observed that the peaks are split. This is caused by the interaction of the magnetic fields of the hydrogen atoms on neighbouring atoms with the applied magnetic field. If the field caused by one hydrogen atom is aligned with the applied field, it reinforces it. If it is opposed, it weakens the applied field. The result is that the peak of a neighbouring hydrogen atom is split.
- Consider the fragment $=CH–CH_2–$
  - The CH hydrogen atom can have its field aligned, ↑, or opposed, ↓. This causes the peak due to the hydrogen atoms in the CH_2 group to split into two.
  - The two CH_2 hydrogen atoms can have three arrangements of field: ↑↑, ↑↓ or ↓↓. This causes the peak due to the CH hydrogen to split into three.
- The splitting due to a $CH_3–CH_2–$ part in a molecule is into a triplet and a quartet.

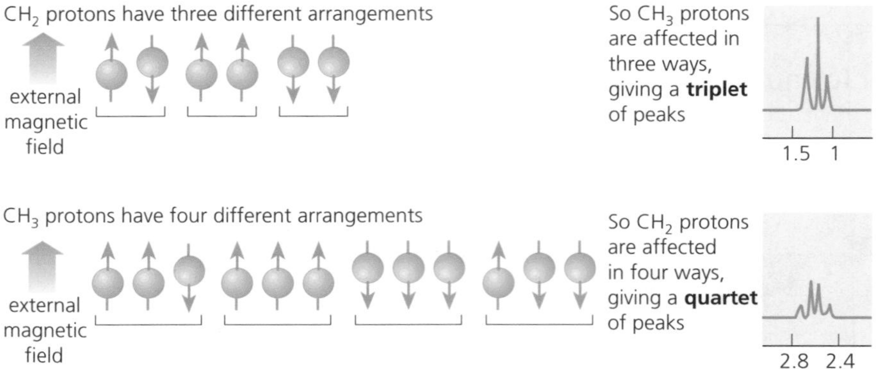

Spin–spin splitting in ethylbenzene

Splitting rule

If the proton of a hydrogen atom has n hydrogen atoms as nearest neighbours, its absorption peaks will be split into (n + 1) lines.

LABILE HYDROGEN ATOMS

- The hydrogen atom in an OH or NH group has no effect and is not affected by any neighbouring hydrogen atoms. It is said to be **labile**.

Effect of adding D_2O

- Labile hydrogen atoms can be detected using water made from hydrogen's isotope, deuterium. On adding D_2O, an exchange reaction takes place:

  $2R–OH + D_2O \rightarrow 2R–OD + H_2O$
- The labile hydrogen on the OH group disappears and so does its NMR peak. This is how labile hydrogen atoms are identified.

Spectra of molecules with labile hydrogen atoms

- The spectrum of ethanol, CH_3CH_2OH, has three sets of peaks at different chemical shifts:
  - The peak at $\delta = 1.1$, due to the CH_3 hydrogen atoms, is split into three by the neighbouring two CH_2 hydrogen atoms.
  - The peak at $\delta = 3.8$, due to the CH_2 hydrogen atoms, is split into four by the three neighbouring hydrogen atoms of the CH_3 group.
  - The peak at $\delta = 5.8$ is due to the OH hydrogen atom and is not split because it is labile, nor does it cause any splitting of the hydrogen atoms in the neighbouring CH_2 group.

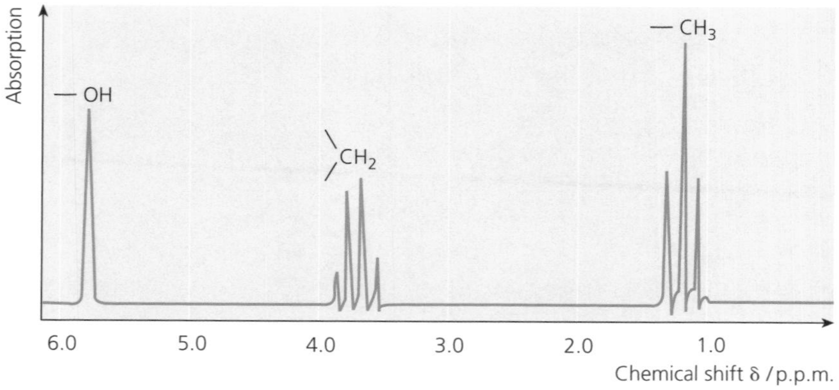

High-resolution NMR spectrum of ethanol

end AQA and OCR only

CHEMICAL ANALYSIS AND SYNTHESIS

CHEMICAL TESTS

ALKENES
- They turn bromine water from brown to colourless.
- They turn purple potassium manganate(VII) in neutral solution to a brown precipitate.

ALCOHOLS
- They give steamy fumes of hydrogen chloride with phosphorus pentachloride.
- They give a fruity smelling product when warmed with a carboxylic acid and concentrated sulphuric acid.
- 1° and 2° alcohols turn orange potassium dichromate(VI) in acid solution green when heated. 3° alcohols have no reaction and so the potassium dichromate stays orange.
- Ethanol and alcohols containing the $CH_3CH(OH)$ group give a pale yellow precipitate of iodoform, CHI_3, when warmed with iodine in aqueous sodium hydroxide.

HALOGENOALKANES
- They give a precipitate when warmed with aqueous sodium hydroxide containing a little ethanol followed by adding nitric acid and aqueous silver nitrate.
- Chloro-compounds give a white precipitate, soluble in dilute ammonia.
- Bromo-compounds give a cream precipitate insoluble in dilute ammonia, but soluble in conc. ammonia.
- Iodo-compounds give a yellow precipitate, insoluble in dilute or conc. ammonia.

ALDEHYDES
- They give an orange/yellow precipitate when a solution of 2,4-dinitrophenylhydrazine (Brady's Reagent) is added.
- They give a silver mirror when warmed with Tollens' reagent (a solution of silver nitrate in alkali and ammonia).
- They give a red precipitate when warmed with Fehling's solution (or Benedict's solution).

If the precipitate with 2,4-dinitrophenylhydrazine is purified and dried, its melting point can be used to identify the aldehyde or ketone.

KETONES
- They give an orange/yellow precipitate when a solution of 2,4-dinitrophenylhydrazine (Brady's Reagent) is added.
- They have no reaction with Tollens' reagent, or with Fehling's solution.
- Methyl ketones, which contain the CH_3CO group, give a pale yellow precipitate of iodoform, CHI_3, when warmed with iodine in aqueous sodium hydroxide.

CARBOXYLIC ACIDS
- They give steamy fumes of hydrogen chloride with phosphorus pentachloride.
- They give off carbon dioxide when added to solutions of sodium carbonate or sodium hydrogencarbonate.
- They give a fruity smelling product when warmed with an alcohol and concentrated sulphuric acid.
- Solutions will turn litmus red.

PHENOL
- It rapidly turns brown bromine water to a white precipitate in a colourless solution.
- It dissolves in sodium carbonate solution without giving off carbon dioxide.

AMINES
- They turn damp litmus blue.

REAGENTS WHICH DO NOT GIVE A CLEAR INFERENCE

PHOSPHORUS PENTACHLORIDE

- This gives steamy fumes with acids as well as with alcohols.
- It also gives steamy fumes with water, so the organic reagents must be dry when using this test.

POTASSIUM DICHROMATE(VI)

- This goes green when warmed in acid solution with primary and secondary alcohols and with other substances that can be oxidised, such as aldehydes.

POTASSIUM MANGANATE(VII)

- In neutral solution, it will rapidly oxidise alkenes to diols and aldehydes to acids. It will also slowly oxidise primary and secondary alcohols on warming.
- In acid solution, it will oxidise aldehydes at room temperature, and primary and secondary alcohols on warming.

2,4-DINITROPHENYLHYDRAZINE

- This gives a yellow/orange precipitate with both aldehydes and ketones.

IODOFORM TEST

- The test is to add iodine solution to aqueous sodium hydroxide until it is slightly coloured, and then the organic substance is added and the mixture warmed. A pale yellow precipitate of triiodomethane (iodoform) is obtained with ethanol, all secondary alcohols with a $CH_3CH(OH)$ group, ethanal and all ketones with a CH_3CO group.

ORGANIC SYNTHETIC ROUTES

Some of the more useful reactions for questions that require a route for making one compound from another in more than one step:

FORMATION OF A NEW C–C BOND

- The carbon chain length can be increased in several ways.

Use of KCN

- Potassium cyanide will react with halogenoalkanes in a substitution reaction:
  $CH_3CH_2Br + KCN \rightarrow CH_3CH_2CN + KBr$
- Conditions: heat under reflux in a solution of ethanol and water.
- Potassium cyanide does not react with alcohols.

Use of HCN

- Hydrogen cyanide adds with aldehydes and ketones:
  $CH_3CHO + HCN \rightarrow CH_3CH(OH)CN$
- Conditions: mix with a catalyst of KCN – or have the mixture buffered at pH = 8.

The nitrile formed can be hydrolysed (by refluxing with aqueous acid) to a carboxylic acid, or reduced (with $NaBH_4$ or $LiAlH_4$) to a primary amine.

Use of Grignard reagents (Edexcel only)

- Grignard reagents react with carbon dioxide to form a carboxylic acid with one more carbon atom:
  $CH_3CH_2MgBr + CO_2 \longrightarrow CH_3CH_2COOH$
- They also react with aldehydes and ketones to form alcohols:
  $CH_3CH_2MgBr + CH_3CHO \longrightarrow CH_3CH_2CH(OH)CH_3$
- Conditions: mix in dry ether solution and then hydrolyse the intermediate with acid.

SUBSTITUTION

- Halogenoalkanes can be converted to alcohols:
  $CH_3CHBrCH_3 + NaOH \rightarrow CH_3CH(OH)CH_3 + NaBr$
- Conditions: reflux with aqueous sodium hydroxide and some ethanol.
- Alcohols can be converted to halogenoalkanes:
  $CH_3CH(OH)CH_3 + PCl_5 \rightarrow CH_3CHClCH_3 + POCl_3 + HCl$
- Use 50% H_2SO_4 + KBr for bromination, or damp red phosphorus and iodine for iodination.

THE THIRD PERIOD – SODIUM TO ARGON

TRENDS IN A PERIOD

- The number of electrons in the outer orbit increases.
- The atomic radius decreases.
- There is a general increase in **1st ionisation energy** with troughs at Al and S.
- The bonding goes from forming cations only (Na and Mg) through cations and covalent bonds (Al) to covalent only (Si and P) to covalent and forming anions (S and Cl). Argon does not form any compounds.
- The elements become less metallic.
- The **electrical conductivity** goes from conducting (Na, Mg, Al) through semi-conducting (Si) to insulating (P, S, Cl and Ar).
- The **melting point** rises Na to Al (metallic structure with charge on ion and number of delocalised electrons increasing) to a maximum at Si (giant atomic lattice with strong covalent bonds between atoms that have to be broken) and then down to P and the other non-metals (intermolecular forces that have to be broken between molecules, P_4 or S_8 or Cl_2 – the strength of these forces depends on the number of electrons in the molecule).

REACTIONS OF THE ELEMENTS

REACTIONS WITH OXYGEN

- All the elements burn in the oxygen in the air except chlorine and argon which do not react.

$2Na + O_2 \rightarrow Na_2O_2$ (sodium peroxide)
$2Mg + O_2 \rightarrow 2MgO$
$4Al + 3O_2 \rightarrow 2Al_2O_3$
} metals form ionic oxides

$4P + 5O_2 \rightarrow P_4O_{10}$
$S + O_2 \rightarrow SO_2$
} non-metals form covalent oxides

Aluminium does not react with air as it has a protective oxide layer, but it burns when strongly heated.

REACTIONS WITH CHLORINE

- All the elements, except argon, react with chlorine.

$2Na + Cl_2 \rightarrow 2NaCl$
$Mg + Cl_2 \rightarrow MgCl_2$
} ionic chlorides

$2Al + 3Cl_2 \rightarrow Al_2Cl_6$
$Si + 2Cl_2 \rightarrow SiCl_4$
$2P + 5Cl_2 \rightarrow 2PCl_5$ (with excess chlorine)
} covalent chlorides

Aluminium chloride is covalent when anhydrous but ionic when hydrated, with the formula $AlCl_3.6H_2O$

REACTIONS WITH WATER

- Only sodium, magnesium and chlorine react.
- Sodium melts and buzzes around on the surface.
  $2Na + 2H_2O \rightarrow 2NaOH + H_2$ pH of final solution = 14
- Magnesium reacts very slowly with cold water.
  $Mg + 2H_2O \rightarrow Mg(OH)_2 + H_2$ pH of final solution = 11
- Chlorine reacts reversibly with water.
  $Cl_2 + H_2O \rightleftharpoons HCl + HOCl$ pH of final solution = 0

PERIOD 3 OXIDES

FORMULAE, BONDING AND ACID–BASE CHARACTER

Element	Formula	Bonding	Acid–base character
sodium	Na_2O (sodium peroxide, Na_2O_2, also exists)	Ionic	Base
magnesium	MgO	Ionic	Base
aluminium	Al_2O_3	Ionic	Amphoteric
silicon	SiO_2	Covalent (giant atomic)	Weakly acidic
phosphorus	P_4O_{10}	Covalent (molecular)	Acidic
sulphur	SO_2 SO_3	Covalent (molecular)	Acidic

REACTIONS OF METAL OXIDES WITH WATER, ACIDS AND BASES

Sodium oxide

- Reacts with water to form a solution of sodium hydroxide, pH = 14.
  $Na_2O(s) + H_2O(l) \rightarrow 2Na^+(aq) + 2OH^-(aq)$
- Reacts with acids to form a salt containing sodium cations.
  $Na_2O(s) + 2H^+(aq) \rightarrow 2Na^+(aq) + H_2O(l)$
- Does not react with bases.

Magnesium oxide

- Reacts partially with water to form a suspension of magnesium hydroxide, pH = 11.
  $MgO(s) + H_2O(l) \rightleftharpoons Mg(OH)_2(s)$
- Reacts with acids to form a salt containing magnesium cations.
  $MgO(s) + 2H^+(aq) \rightarrow Mg^{2+}(aq) + H_2O(l)$
- Does not react with bases.

Aluminium oxide

- Does not react with water.
- Reacts with acids to form salts containing aluminium cations.
  $Al_2O_3(s) + 6H^+(aq) \rightarrow 2Al^{3+}(aq) + 3H_2O(l)$
- Because it is **amphoteric** it also reacts with bases to form salts with the aluminium in the anion.
  $Al_2O_3(s) + 6OH^-(aq) + 3H_2O(l) \rightarrow 2[Al(OH)_6]^{3-}(aq)$

ACID–BASE REACTIONS OF METAL HYDROXIDES

- Sodium hydroxide is an alkali and reacts with acids.
  $NaOH + HCl \rightarrow NaCl + H_2O$
- Magnesium hydroxide is a base and reacts with acids.
  $Mg(OH)_2 + 2HCl \rightarrow MgCl_2 + 2H_2O$
- Aluminium hydroxide is **amphoteric** so reacts with both acids and bases to form colourless solutions.
  $Al(OH)_3 + 3HCl \rightarrow AlCl_3 + 3H_2O$
  $Al(OH)_3 + 3NaOH \rightarrow Na_3[Al(OH)_6]$

REACTIONS OF NON-METAL OXIDES WITH WATER, ACIDS AND BASES

- All non-metal oxides are acidic and so none reacts with acids.

Silicon dioxide

- Because of its giant atomic lattice, it does not react with water and only reacts slowly with hot concentrated sodium hydroxide.
  $SiO_2 + 2NaOH \rightarrow Na_2SiO_3 + H_2O$

Phosphorus(V) oxide

- With water it forms a solution of phosphoric(V) acid. $P_4O_{10} + 6H_2O \rightarrow 4H_3PO_4$ pH = 2
- With sodium hydroxide it forms sodium phosphate. $P_4O_{10} + 12NaOH \rightarrow 4Na_3PO_4 + 6H_2O$

Sulphur dioxide

- With water it forms sulphurous acid (sulphuric(IV) acid) and with alkalis it forms a sulphite (sulphate(IV)).
  $SO_2 + H_2O \rightleftharpoons H_2SO_3$ pH = 3
  $SO_2(g) + 2OH^-(aq) \rightarrow SO_3^{2-}(aq) + H_2O(l)$

Sulphur trioxide

- With water it forms sulphuric acid and with alkalis it forms sulphates.
  $SO_3 + H_2O \rightarrow H_2SO_4$ pH = 0
  $SO_3(aq) + 2OH^-(aq) \rightarrow SO_4^{2-}(aq) + H_2O(l)$

PERIOD 3 CHLORIDES

FORMULAE AND BONDING

Element	Formula	Bonding
sodium	$NaCl$	Ionic
magnesium	$MgCl_2$	Ionic
aluminium	$AlCl_3.6H_2O$ Al_2Cl_6	Ionic Covalent
silicon	$SiCl_4$	Covalent
phosphorus	PCl_3 PCl_5	Covalent Covalent

REACTIONS OF IONIC CHLORIDES WITH WATER

- Sodium chloride and magnesium chloride dissolve to give neutral solutions, pH = 7.
  $NaCl(s) + aq \rightarrow Na^+(aq) + Cl^-(aq)$
  $MgCl_2(s) + aq \rightarrow Mg^{2+}(aq) + 2Cl^-(aq)$
- Hydrated aluminium chloride is hydrolysed by water. The $[Al(H_2O)_6]^{3+}$ ions produced by dissolving the $AlCl_3.6H_2O$ are deprotonated by the water solvent to give a solution of pH = 2.
  $[Al(H_2O)_6]^{3+}(aq) + H_2O(l) \rightleftharpoons [Al(H_2O)_5OH]^{2+}(aq) + H_3O^+(aq)$

REACTIONS OF COVALENT CHLORIDES WITH WATER

- Covalent chlorides are all rapidly hydrolysed when some water is added. Hydrogen chloride is produced, often as steamy fumes, and an oxide or oxyacid is left. The resulting solutions are highly acidic, pH = 0.
  $Al_2Cl_6 + 3H_2O \rightarrow Al_2O_3 + 6HCl$
  $SiCl_4 + 2H_2O \rightarrow SiO_2 + 4HCl$
  $PCl_3 + 3H_2O \rightarrow H_3PO_3 + 3HCl$
  $PCl_5 + 4H_2O \rightarrow H_3PO_4 + 5HCl$

- Phosphorus pentachloride also reacts with alcohols and carboxylic acids to produce HCl fumes. These organic compounds have an OH group as does water.
  $PCl_5 + C_2H_5OH \rightarrow C_2H_5Cl + HCl + POCl_3$

- Aluminium has chemical properties of both metals and non-metals.
  - Its oxide and hydroxide are **amphoteric** – react with both acids and bases.
  - Its hydrated chloride is ionic but is partially hydrolysed.
  - Its anhydrous chloride is covalent and reacts with water, as do other covalent chlorides.

KEY POINTS

- Metal oxides (and hydroxides) are ionic and are bases.
- Non-metal oxides are covalent and are acidic.
- Metal chlorides are ionic and dissolve in water.
- Non-metal chlorides are covalent and react with water to form hydrogen chloride.

GROUP 4

start Edexcel only

CONDUCTION OF ELECTRICITY

The general trend is for the conduction to increase down the Group.

- The diamond allotrope of carbon does not conduct.
- Graphite does conduct – because of its unique structure of delocalised π electrons above and below the hexagonal rings of carbon atoms.
- Silicon and germanium are semi-conductors.
- Tin and lead show the electrical conduction typical of metals.

RELATIVE STABILITY OF THE +2 AND +4 STATES

The trend is for the +2 state to become more stable than the +4 state down the Group.

Tin

Tin is more stable in the +4 state than in the +2 state.

- Tin(II) compounds are strongly reducing and so are easily oxidised to the +4 state.
- Tin(II) ions will reduce Fe^{3+} ion to Fe^{2+}
  $Sn^{2+}(aq) + 2Fe^{3+}(aq) \rightarrow Sn^{4+}(aq) + 2Fe^{2+}(aq)$
  and will reduce iodine to iodide ions.
  $Sn^{2+}(aq) + I_2(s) \rightarrow Sn^{4+}(aq) + 2I^-(aq)$

Lead

Lead is more stable in the +2 state than in the +4 state.

- Lead(IV) compounds are strongly oxidising.
- They will oxidise Fe^{2+} ions to Fe^{3+}
  $PbO_2 + 2Fe^{2+} + 4H^+ \rightarrow Pb^{2+} + 2Fe^{3+} + 2H_2O$
  and hydrogen chloride to chlorine.
  $PbO_2 + 4HCl \rightarrow PbCl_2 + Cl_2 + 2H_2O$
- The following reaction shows that lead is more stable in the +2 state than in the +4 state.
  $PbCl_4 + SnCl_2 \rightarrow PbCl_2 + SnCl_4$
  +4 +2 +2 +4

The reaction goes from left to right – reduction of lead(IV) and oxidation of tin(II) – and not from right to left – oxidation of lead(II) and reduction of tin(IV).

ACID–BASE PROPERTIES OF THE OXIDES

Trend down the Group for oxides: weakly acidic → amphoteric

- Carbon dioxide and silicon dioxide are weakly acidic.
- Carbon dioxide reacts reversibly with water to form carbonic acid, which is a weak acid: pH = 5.
  $CO_2 + H_2O \rightleftharpoons H_2CO_3 \rightleftharpoons H^+ + HCO_3^-$
- It reacts with bases such as sodium hydroxide to form a carbonate.
  $CO_2 + 2NaOH \rightarrow Na_2CO_3 + H_2O$
- Silicon dioxide has a giant atomic structure and so has too high an activation energy to react noticeably with dilute sodium hydroxide. However, it reacts with hot concentrated or molten sodium hydroxide.
  $SiO_2 + 2NaOH \rightarrow Na_2SiO_3 + H_2O$
- Tin and lead each form amphoteric oxides, which react with both acids and bases.
  $PbO + 2HCl \rightarrow PbCl_2 + H_2O$
  $PbO + 2NaOH + H_2O \rightarrow Na_2[Pb(OH)_4]$

end Edexcel only

HYDROLYSIS OF CCl_4 AND $SiCl_4$

- When water is added to $SiCl_4$, a lone pair of electrons on the oxygen forms a dative covalent bond with an empty 3d orbital in silicon. The bond energy released is sufficient to cause a Si–Cl bond to break. This process continues until all the Si–Cl bonds have been broken.
- The carbon in CCl_4 does not have any 2d orbitals and so cannot accept a pair of electrons from the water. Also, the small carbon atom is completely surrounded by the much larger chlorine atoms. This means that water molecules cannot attack the carbon atom in an S_N2 reaction, as happens with halogenoalkanes (see 'Mechanisms', page 82), so CCl_4 does not react with water.

THE TRANSITION ELEMENTS

ELECTRONIC CONFIGURATION

The elements from scandium to zinc, and those below them in the Periodic Table, are called the **d block elements** because the d orbitals are being filled.

Electronic configuration of transition elements and their most stable ions

Element	Electronic configuration of atom	Electronic configuration of ion
scandium	Sc [Ar] $4s^2$ $3d^1$	Sc^{3+} [Ar] $4s^0$ $3d^0$
titanium	Ti [Ar] $4s^2$ $3d^2$	Ti^{4+} [Ar] $4s^0$ $3d^0$
vanadium	V [Ar] $4s^2$ $3d^3$	V^{3+} [Ar] $4s^0$ $3d^2$
chromium	Cr [Ar] **$4s^1$ $3d^5$**	Cr^{3+} [Ar] $4s^0$ $3d^3$
manganese	Mn [Ar] $4s^2$ $3d^5$	Mn^{2+} [Ar] $4s^0$ $3d^5$
iron	Fe [Ar] $4s^2$ $3d^6$	Fe^{2+} [Ar] $4s^0$ $3d^6$
		Fe^{3+} [Ar] $4s^0$ $3d^5$
cobalt	Co [Ar] $4s^2$ $3d^7$	Co^{2+} [Ar] $4s^0$ $3d^7$
nickel	Ni [Ar] $4s^2$ $3d^8$	Ni^{2+} [Ar] $4s^0$ $3d^8$
copper	Cu [Ar] **$4s^1$ $3d^{10}$**	Cu^{+} [Ar] $4s^0$ $3d^{10}$
		Cu^{2+} [Ar] $4s^0$ $3d^9$
zinc	Zn [Ar] $4s^2$ $3d^{10}$	Zn^{2+} [Ar] $4s^0$ $3d^{10}$

[Ar] is the electronic configuration of Argon: $1s^22s^22p^63s^23p^6$

Note the stability of half-filled d orbitals, Cr, Mn^{2+} and Fe^{3+} and of fully-filled d orbitals, Cu and Zn^{2+}

- Cations are formed by first losing the 4s electrons and only then are d electrons lost.
- This causes the ion to be smaller (resulting in a larger lattice enthalpy or hydration enthalpy) than if it just lost its d electrons.

DEFINITION

A transition metal is one which has incompletely filled d orbitals in one of its cations.

Scandium only forms 3+ ions (no d electrons) and zinc only forms 2+ ions (all five d orbitals full) so neither is a transition metal.

CHARACTERISTIC PROPERTIES OF TRANSITION METALS

- **Different oxidation states**
- **Coloured ions**
- **They form complex ions**
- **They are catalysts**

Colours of ions in different oxidation states

Element	Oxidation state	Ions	Colour
vanadium	+2	$[V(H_2O)_6]^{2+}$	Purple
	+3	$[V(H_2O)_6]^{3+}$	Green
	+4	VO^{2+}	Blue
	+5	VO_2^{+}	Yellow
chromium	+3	$[Cr(H_2O)_6]^{3+}$	Green
	+6	CrO_4^{2-}	Yellow
manganese	+2	$[Mn(H_2O)_6]^{2+}$	Pale pink
	+7	MnO_4^{-}	Deep purple
iron	+2	$[Fe(H_2O)_6]^{2+}$	Pale green
	+3	$[Fe(H_2O)_6]^{3+}$	Amethyst
cobalt	+2	$[Co(H_2O)_6]^{2+}$	Pink
nickel	+2	$[Ni(H_2O)_6]^{2+}$	Green
copper	+1	$[Cu(H_2O)_6]^{+}$	Colourless
	+2	$[Cu(H_2O)_6]^{2+}$	Blue

COMPOUNDS IN DIFFERENT OXIDATION STATES

- Transition metals can use a different number of electrons in bonding and so exist in a variety of oxidation states.
- The successive ionisation energies go up steadily – as shown here for iron.

1st	2nd	3rd
762	1510	2960

- The energy required to remove a third electron from a Fe^{2+} ion is regained by the energy released forming the hydrated ion or the lattice enthalpy of the solid. Thus iron exists in both the +2 and the +3 oxidation state.
- Transition metals, such as manganese, can use up to seven of their 4s and 3d electrons and form seven covalent bonds as in the MnO_4^- ion where the manganese is doubly bonded to three oxygen atoms and singly bonded to the fourth.

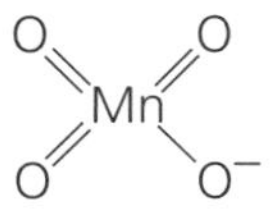

COMPLEX IONS

- Species with a lone pair of electrons can form dative covalent bonds with empty 4s, 3d and 4p orbitals in a transition metal ion. The result is a complex ion in which usually six molecules or ions are datively bonded on to the central metal ion.
- Typical species which bond with transition metal ions to form complex ions are H_2O, NH_3, Cl^- and CN^-. The species that bond in this way are called **ligands**. The number of dative covalent bonds formed by ligands is called the **co-ordination number** of the transition metal ion.

- Most ligands have one atom with a lone pair of electrons that forms **one** dative covalent bond with the transition metal ion.
- Some have two atoms with lone pairs and so can form two dative bonds. These are called **bidentate** ligands.
- Diaminoethane, $NH_2CH_2CH_2NH_2$ is an example where both nitrogen atoms form dative bonds with the same transition metal ion.
- The $EDTA^{4-}$ ion, $(^-OOCCH_2)_2NCH_2CH_2N(CH_2COO^-)_2$, has two nitrogen atoms and four COO^- groups and so can form six ligands. This is a **polydentate** ligand.

- The charge on a complex ion can be calculated by adding together the charge on the transition metal ion and the charge, if any, on the ligands.
- The hexacyano-iron(III) $[Fe(CN)_6]^{3-}$ ion has a charge of $+3 + (6 \times -1) = -3$.

Co-ordination number of 6

- Most transition metal ions form complexes with six ligands. Examples are:
  - the hydrated cations, such as $[Fe(H_2O)_6]^{2+}$
  - ammonia complexes, such as $[Cu(NH_3)_4(H_2O)_2]^{2+}$
  - anions, such as $[Cr(OH)_6]^{3-}$ and $[Fe(CN)_6]^{3-}$
- All complexes with a co-ordination number of six are octahedral.
- The six pairs of bonding electrons around the transition metal ion repel each other and take up a position of maximum separation, which is an octahedral shape.

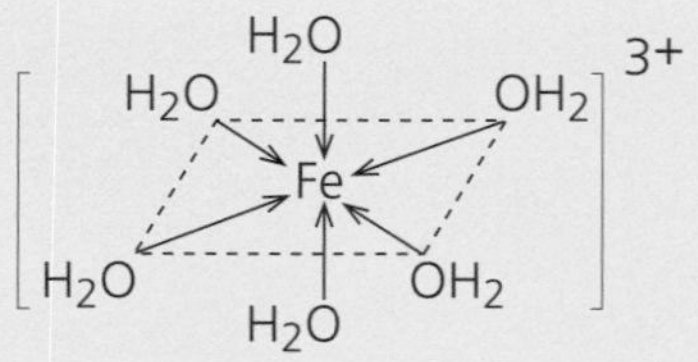

Co-ordination number of 4

- Large ligands, such as Cl^-, usually form four co-ordinate complexes. An example is $[CuCl_4]^{2-}$, which is tetrahedral. The anti-cancer drug *cis*-platin, $[Pt(NH_3)_2Cl_2]$, is square planar.

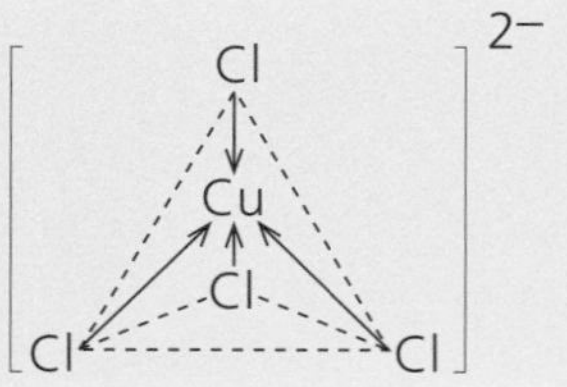

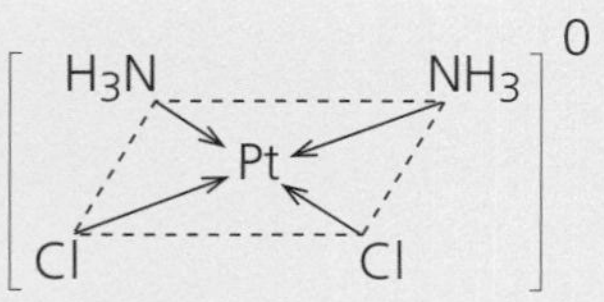

Co-ordination number of 2

- Silver forms complexes with this co-ordination number, such as $[Ag(NH_3)_2]^+$. This is the complex ion present in Tollens' reagent which is reduced to a silver mirror by aldehydes. It is linear in shape.

COLOURED IONS

- In hydrated or complexed ions, the five d orbitals are split into a set of three at a lower energy level and a set of two at an upper level. The colour is caused by light of a specific colour being **absorbed** and its energy being used to promote a d electron from one of the lower levels to an unfilled higher level. To be able to do this the ion must have at least one d electron and at least one partially-filled d orbital.
- Ti^{4+} has no d electrons and so is colourless. Cu^{+} (and Zn^{2+}) has all its d orbitals filled and is also colourless.
- The colour of the ion is the complementary colour – if orange light is absorbed, the ion will be blue.

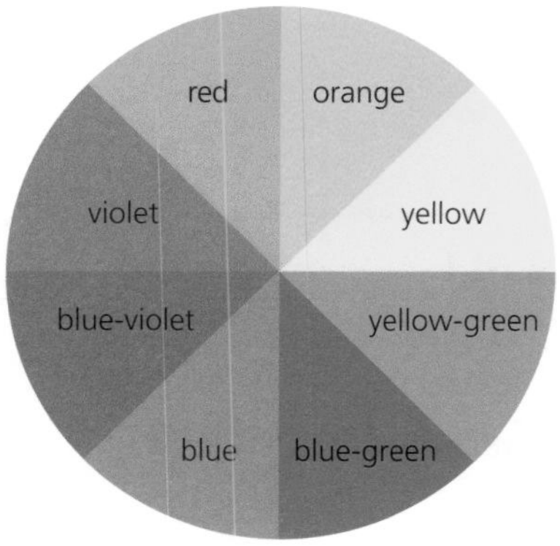

Colour wheel – complimentary colours are opposite one another

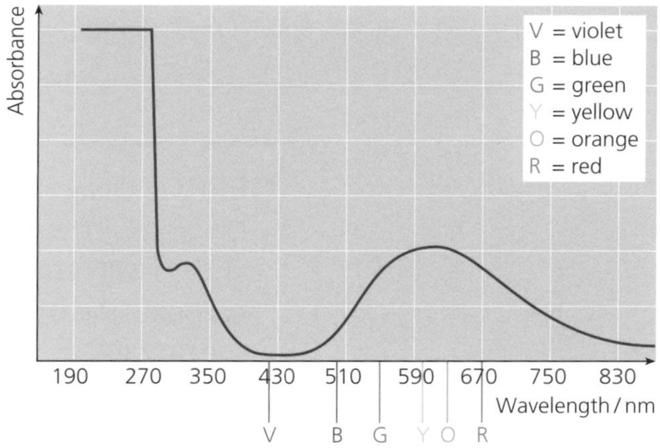

Absorption of coloured light by the $[Cu(NH_3)_4(H_2O)_2]^{2+}$ ion

CATALYSTS

- Many transition metals or their compounds are catalysts. Examples include:
  - iron in the Haber Process
  - vanadium(V) oxide in the manufacture of sulphuric acid
  - nickel in the addition of hydrogen to alkenes.
- Catalysts work in one of two ways.

Adsorption

- They adsorb a gaseous reactant using empty d orbitals to form partial bonds with the adsorbed gas.
- For example, nickel adsorbs hydrogen by splitting the H_2 molecule. The atoms then bind into the spaces between the nickel atoms.

Intermediate formation

- They react with one of the substances and form an intermediate compound.
- Transition metal compounds can do this because they exist in different oxidation states.
- For example, vanadium(V) oxide reacts with sulphur dioxide to form the intermediate vanadium(IV) oxide, which then reacts with oxygen to reform vanadium(V) oxide.
  - Step 1: $V_2O_5 + SO_2 \rightarrow 2VO_2 + SO_3$
  - Step 2: $2VO_2 + \frac{1}{2}O_2 \rightarrow V_2O_5$
- Another example: Fe^{2+} ions are the catalyst in the oxidation of I^- ions by persulphate ions, $S_2O_8^{2-}$, the intermediate being the Fe^{3+} ion.
  - Step 1: $2Fe^{2+} + S_2O_8^{2-} \rightarrow 2SO_4^{2-} + 2Fe^{3+}$
  - Step 2: $2Fe^{3+} + 2I^- \rightarrow 2Fe^{2+} + I_2$

The Fe^{2+} catalyst prevents the need for a collision between two negative ions.

REACTIONS OF AQUA-IONS

DEPROTONATION BY WATER

- The solvent water molecules can remove a proton from the water molecules that are the ligands in the aqua-ions.
- The result is that the solution becomes acidic, due to the production of H_3O^+ ions.
- This happens to a greater extent with 3+ ions than with 2+ ions, because the higher charge draws electrons from the water towards the transition metal ion – polarising the water molecule.

$[Fe(H_2O)_6]^{3+}(aq) + H_2O(l) \rightleftharpoons [Fe(H_2O)_5OH]^{2+}(aq) + H_3O^+(aq)$ pH = 2

$[Fe(H_2O)_6]^{2+}(aq) + H_2O(l) \rightleftharpoons [Fe(H_2O)_5OH]^{+}(aq) + H_3O^+(aq)$ pH = 4

DEPROTONATION BY AN ALKALI

- OH^- ions are a much stronger base than H_2O molecules, and so will remove H^+ from the water molecules in the complex ion until a neutral species is produced as a precipitate.
  $[Fe(H_2O)_6]^{3+}(aq) + 3OH^-(aq) \rightarrow [Fe(H_2O)_3(OH)_3](s) + 3H_2O(l)$
  forming a red precipitate of hydrated iron(III) hydroxide.
  $[Fe(H_2O)_6]^{2+}(aq) + 2OH^-(aq) \rightarrow [Fe(H_2O)_4(OH)_2](s) + 2H_2O(l)$
  forming a green precipitate of hydrated iron(II) hydroxide.
- Some d block metals are so polarising that further deprotonation can take place and the initial hydrated hydroxide precipitate 'dissolves' in excess alkali. These are the **amphoteric** metal hydroxides (see the table below).
- Chromium ions first form a green precipitate which dissolves in excess sodium hydroxide to form a green solution.
  $[Cr(H_2O)_6]^{3+}(aq) + 3OH^-(aq) \rightarrow [Cr(H_2O)_3(OH)_3](s) + 3H_2O(l)$
  $[Cr(H_2O)_3(OH)_3](s) + 3OH^-(aq) \rightarrow [Cr(OH)_6]^{3-}(aq) + 3H_2O(l)$

Effect adding aqueous sodium hydroxide

Ion	Addition of some NaOH	Addition of excess NaOH
$[Cr(H_2O)_6]^{3+}$	Green precipitate	Green solution of $[Cr(OH)_6]^{3-}$
$[Mn(H_2O)_6]^{2+}$	Sandy precipitate *	No change
$[Fe(H_2O)_6]^{2+}$	Dirty green precipitate **	No change
$[Fe(H_2O)_6]^{3+}$	Foxy-red precipitate	No change
$[Co(H_2O)_6]^{2+}$	Blue precipitate turning pink	Slow reaction forming $[Co(OH)_4]^-$
$[Ni(H_2O)_6]^{2+}$	Green precipitate	No change
$[Cu(H_2O)_6]^{2+}$	Blue precipitate	No change
$[Zn(H_2O)_6]^{2+}$	White precipitate	Colourless solution of $[Zn(OH)_4]^{2-}$

* This slowly darkens as it is oxidised by air to manganese(IV) oxide.

** This slowly goes brown-red as it is oxidised by air to iron(III) hydroxide.

REPLACEMENT BY Cl^- IONS

- When concentrated HCl is added to aqueous copper(II) sulphate solution, **ligand exchange** takes place, and the solution turns from blue to yellow.

$[Cu(H_2O)_6]^{2+}(aq) + 4Cl^-(aq) \rightarrow [CuCl_4]^{2-} + 6H_2O(l)$

blue — yellow

OTHER REPLACEMENT REACTIONS

- Cyanide ions, CN^-, will replace water ligands in many aqua-ions.

$[Fe(H_2O)_6]^{3+}(aq) + 6CN^-(aq) \rightarrow [Fe(CN)_6]^{3-}(aq) + 6H_2O(l)$

- $EDTA^{4-}$ ions will ligand exchange with many other complexes.

$[Cu(H_2O)_6]^{2+}(aq) + EDTA^{4-}(aq) \rightarrow [CuEDTA]^{2-}(aq) + 6H_2O(l)$

LIGAND EXCHANGE

This is a reaction in which the ligands around the transition metal ion are totally or partially replaced by other ligands.

REPLACEMENT BY NH_3

- When aqueous ammonia solution is added to a solution of hydrated d block ions, a precipitate of the hydrated hydroxide is first obtained.

$[Fe(H_2O)_6]^{3+}(aq) + 3NH_3(aq) \rightarrow [Fe(H_2O)_3(OH)_3](s) + 3NH_4^+(aq)$

$[Cu(H_2O)_6]^{2+}(aq) + 2NH_3(aq) \rightarrow [Cu(H_2O)_4(OH)_2](s) + 2NH_4^+(aq)$

- In some cases these precipitates react with excess ammonia in a ligand exchange reaction.

$[Ni(H_2O)_4(OH)_2](s) + 4NH_3(aq) \rightarrow [Ni(NH_3)_4(H_2O)_2]^{2+} + 2H_2O(l) + 2OH^-(aq)$

green precipitate — green solution

$[Cu(H_2O)_4(OH)_2](s) + 4NH_3(aq) \rightarrow [Cu(NH_3)_4(H_2O)_2]^{2+} + 2H_2O(l) + 2OH^-(aq)$

blue precipitate — deep blue solution

$[Zn(H_2O)_4(OH)_2](s) + 4NH_3(aq) \rightarrow [Zn(NH_3)_4(H_2O)_2]^{2+} + 2H_2O(l) + 2OH^-(aq)$

white precipitate — colourless solution

COLOUR CHANGES IN COMPLEXES

- The colour of a complex ion depends on:
  - the transition metal
  - its oxidation state
  - the ligands.
- The extent of the splitting of the *d* orbitals is altered if either the ligand or the charge on the ion changes.

Change of ligand

- When the H_2O ligands in hydrated copper(II) ions are replaced by Cl^- ions, the solution turns from blue to yellow.
- $[Fe(H_2O)_6]^{3+}$ ions are amethyst whereas $[Fe(H_2O)_5OH]^{2+}$ ions are brown and $[Fe(H_2O)_5SCN]^{2+}$ ions are blood red.

Change of oxidation state

- Hydrated iron(III) ions, $[Fe(H_2O)_6]^{3+}$, are amethyst whereas iron(II) ions, $[Fe(H_2O)_6]^{2+}$, are pale green.
- Chromium(III) ions, $[Cr(H_2O)_6]^{3+}$, are green whereas $[Cr(H_2O)_6]^{2+}$ ions are blue and chromate(VI) ions, CrO_4^{2-}, are yellow.
- Copper(II) complexes are blue or yellow whereas all copper(I) complexes are colourless. This is because in copper(I) compounds all the d orbitals are full.

REDOX REACTIONS

- Hydrogen peroxide in alkaline solution will oxidise Cr^{3+} to CrO_4^{2-}.

$2Cr^{3+} + 3H_2O_2 + 10OH^- \rightarrow 2CrO_4^{2-} + 8H_2O$

+3 (Cr) → +6 (Cr); −1 × 2 (O) → −2 (O)

The oxidation number of chromium changes by +3, and there are two of them.
Each oxygen changes by −1, and there are six of them.
So the total change of oxidation number of both elements is six.

- The oxygen in air will oxidise Co^{2+} in the presence of ammonia to form an ammonia complex of cobalt(III).
- Manganate(VII) ions and dichromate(VI) ions in acid solution are powerful oxidising agents and will oxidise iodide ions to iodine and alcohols to ketones or carboxylic acids.

start

Edexcel and Nuffield only

VANADIUM CHEMISTRY

The electronic configuration of vanadium is [Ar] $4s^2\ 3d^3$.

VARIABLE OXIDATION STATES (Edexcel only)

- Vanadium has compounds in four different oxidation states:

  +5 state VO_3^- (colourless) and VO_2^+ (yellow)
  +4 state VO^{2+} (blue)
  +3 state V^{3+} (green)
  +2 state V^{2+} (purple or lavender)

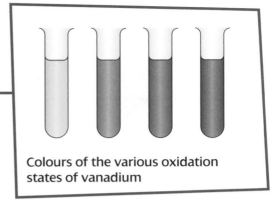

Colours of the various oxidation states of vanadium

REDOX REACTIONS (Edexcel and Nuffield only)

- For a redox reaction to work, the E_{cell} must be positive.
- Remember that the E value for the half-reaction containing the reducing agent has to be reversed – the reducing agent is the substance being oxidised.

Reduction of vanadium compounds

- Zinc, in acid solution, will reduce vanadium(V) down to vanadium(II), with the following colour changes.

yellow	green	blue	green	purple
VO_2^+	VO_2^+ and VO^{2+}	VO^{2+}	V^{3+}	V^{2+}

- Fe^{2+} will reduce VO_2^+ to VO^{2+} but no further as can be seen from the $E^\ominus$ values.

$VO_2^+ + 2H^+ + e^- \rightleftharpoons VO^{2+} + H_2O$ $E^\ominus = +1.0\ V$
$Fe^{3+} + e^- \rightleftharpoons Fe^{2+}$ $E^\ominus = +0.77\ V$
$VO^{2+} + 2H^+ + e^- \rightleftharpoons V^{3+} + H_2O$ $E^\ominus = +0.34\ V$

$E_{cell} = +0.23\ V$ (first and second)
$E_{cell} = -0.33\ V$ (second and third) – Negative, so no reaction

- Sn^{2+} will reduce VO_2^+ to V^{3+} because both E_{cell} values are positive.

$VO_2^+ + 2H^+ + e^- \rightleftharpoons VO^{2+} + H_2O$ $E^\ominus = +1.0\ V$
$Sn^{4+} + 2e^- \rightleftharpoons Sn^{2+}$ $E^\ominus = +0.15\ V$
$VO^{2+} + 2H^+ + e^- \rightleftharpoons V^{3+} + H_2O$ $E^\ominus = +0.34\ V$

$E_{cell} = +0.85\ V$ (first and second)
$E_{cell} = +0.19\ V$ (second and third)

Oxidation of vanadium compounds

- V^{3+} is oxidised to VO^{2+} by Fe^{3+} ions ($E_{cell} = +0.33\ V$).
- VO^{2+} is oxidised to VO_2^+ by Cl_2.

$Cl_2 + 2e^- \rightleftharpoons 2Cl^-$ $E^\ominus = +1.36\ V$
$VO_2^+ + 2H^+ + e^- \rightleftharpoons VO^{2+} + H_2O$ $E^\ominus = +1.0\ V$

$E_{cell} = +0.36\ V$

end

Edexcel and Nuffield only

INDEX